RECENT RESEARCH
in
MOLECULAR BEAMS

RECENT RESEARCH

in

MOLECULAR BEAMS

A Collection of Papers
Dedicated to

OTTO STERN

On the Occasion of his
Seventieth Birthday

Edited by
IMMANUEL ESTERMANN
Office of Naval Research, Washington, D. C.

1959
ACADEMIC PRESS, NEW YORK AND LONDON

ACADEMIC PRESS INC.
111 FIFTH AVENUE
NEW YORK 3, NEW YORK

U.K. Edition, Published by

ACADEMIC PRESS INC. (LONDON) LTD.
40 PALL MALL
LONDON S.W. 1

Library of Congress Catalog Card Number: 59-7924

PRINTED IN GREAT BRITAIN
BY J. W. ARROWSMITH LTD.
WINTERSTOKE ROAD, BRISTOL 3

PREFACE

During the month of February of 1958, Otto Stern, the founder of Molecular Beam Research, completed his seventieth year. This is a landmark that calls for public recognition by his many friends and disciples. The most appropriate way of paying tribute to a scientist on such an occasion is to present a series of scientific papers which have been inspired by his work and have carried it beyond the limits of his own efforts. The papers printed on the following pages have been contributed in this spirit and have been selected with the aim to illustrate the various scientific fields which have been stimulated by Stern's personality and by his work. Some deal with current research on specific problems, some are review papers covering broader areas, and some attempt to describe the early history of molecular beam research in certain laboratories. They do not claim to give a comprehensive account in any of these respects. Their principal objective is to express to Otto Stern the authors' appreciation for the inspiration they found in his work and to wish him, jointly with the numerous other workers in this field of research and with his many friends outside the Molecular Beam Fraternity, many more years of health and happiness.

I. ESTERMANN

1959
Washington, D.C.

TABLE OF CONTENTS

Molecular Beam Research in Hamburg
1922–1933

I. ESTERMANN

Office of Naval Research, Washington, D.C.

Although the first molecular beam experiments were carried out by Dunoyer in 1911,[1] molecular beam research as a planned scientific endeavor began in 1919, when Stern started a series of experiments on the direct determination of the thermal velocity of molecules. The two papers on this subject,[2] which appeared in 1920, were followed in 1921 and 1922 by four papers dealing with the problems of space quantization and atomic magnetic moments.[3] These experiments came at a time when the then new quantum theory, under the leadership of Bohr and Sommerfeld, developed concepts which were in direct contrast with those of classical physics. It was characteristic of Stern's approach to analyze controversial theories and to suggest and perform simple—in principle, if not always in practice—experiments to decide a question in one way or the other. The work described in the papers mentioned above became a classic and is known as the Stern-Gerlach experiment, W. Gerlach having been Stern's collaborator in the last three of these papers. In addition to establishing the reality of Sommerfeld's space quantization, these experiments led to the first direct measurement of an atomic magnetic moment: the moment of the silver atom which was found to be equal to the Bohr magneton, a value predicted theoretically by Bohr for the moment of a hydrogen atom.

In 1922, Stern became professor of physical chemistry at the University of Hamburg, where he began to organize a laboratory devoted mainly to molecular beam research, though occasionally other investigations were carried out there also. Most of the scientific proceedings of this epoch are recorded in a series of thirty papers with the subtitle: "Untersuchungen zur Molekularstrahlmethode" (U.z.M.) which appeared in the *Zeitschrift für Physik* between 1926 and 1933. These papers contain the basic ingredients of the method, and with few exceptions the later and current work can be traced directly or indirectly to their content. In the following paragraphs, I shall try to establish this connection, but before doing so, I would like to make a few observations.

The Hamburg Institute was never very large, and the number of doctoral students associated with it during this period was quite small, about six. Most of the important work was performed by Stern and a number of post-doctoral associates of whom a good fraction were research fellows from foreign countries. It was there where I. I. Rabi was introduced to molecular beam research, which he brought to full bloom after his return to Columbia, and in whose laboratory there most of the present workers received their introduction to the field. Among other guests were Ronald Fraser, who wrote the first monograph[4] on the subject; John B. Taylor, who developed the surface ionization detector, which is still one of the most valuable tools; T. E. Phipps and Emilio Segrè, who together with Stern and Frisch observed the "flops" of atoms in magnetic fields which play such an important part in the current molecular beam technology as applied to atomic, molecular, and nuclear moments and spins.

The highlights of this period were the confirmation of the wave properties of material particles and the quantitative verification of the de Broglie equation $\lambda = h/mv$, and the first measurements of the magnetic moments of the proton and deuteron. But these experiments would not have been possible without the previous painstaking work in which the principles and many experimental details were worked out and checked out, especially in view of the fact that the general level of the relevant technology (vacuum, electronic, etc.) was in its very early stages and that in most cases experimental techniques had to be stretched to the limit.

In the first paper of the U.z.M. series, U.z.M. No. 1, Stern discussed the general principles of the method and also developed a "Program" for its application. The problems listed in this paper as particularly suitable for molecular beam investigations mentioned are

1. Measurements of magnetic moments of atoms or molecules of the order of one Bohr magneton
2. Nuclear and other moments of order of 1/2000 Bohr magneton
3. Moments of higher order
4. "Natural" electric dipole moments of molecules
5. Higher order electric moments
6. Intermolecular forces
7. The radiation reaction according to Einstein
8. The existence of de Broglie waves.

These problems had been attacked with some degree of success during the Hamburg period, though in many cases much more complete and precise work was performed later elsewhere, particularly in Rabi's laboratory at Columbia University and the various laboratories started by Rabi's students, as evidenced by the papers in the present volume.   In addition, several problems not listed in the "Program" were started in Hamburg, and some of them are still of contemporary interest. On the other hand, new techniques and problems were originated after the Hamburg period which make the earlier work appear primitive and unsophisticated, but basically most of the various branches of the current research can be traced to roots planted during this period.

The second paper, U.z.M. No. 2, deals with the technical problem of producing very narrow molecular beams of high intensity, a problem which had been stated in U.z.M. No. 1 as paramount for the various applications.   The principles laid down in this paper are still basic for design of molecular beam equipment.   Other papers dealing essentially with techniques are U.z.M. No. 5, where the equations for the intensity distribution of magnetically deflected beams are developed; U.z.M. No. 10, which describes the handling of beams of permanent gases and the Pirani gauge detector system; and U.z.M. No. 12, which deals with Rabi's first effort in the molecular beam area and discusses a new arrangement for magnetic deflection of molecular beams and its application to the measurement of the magnetic moment of the K atom.   In U.z.M. No. 14 the now famous surface ionization detector and its application to the measurement of the moments of the K and Li atoms are described for the first time.   This detector, though only applicable to atoms and molecules of low ionization potential, is still used extensively and has opened many new avenues to investigation by molecular beam techniques.   Another potentially very powerful detection method based on the destruction of electronic space charge by ions is described in U.z.M. No. 28, but in spite of its universal applicability, it has yet to be utilized for specific investigations.   Experiments dealing with the condensation of molecular beams, the first method used for their detection, were carried out during this period, and reported in several papers not included in the U.z.M. series; they are listed in reference 5. After remaining dormant for many years, this method is currently used again for experiments with radioactive atoms, and other problems, as mentioned in papers Nos. 2 and 9 of this volume.

The other papers will be reviewed in the order of Stern's "program". A group dealing with measurements of magnetic moments of the order of the Bohr magneton by means of the Stern-Gerlach arrangement are

U.z.M. No. 4 (K, Na, Tl), No. 6 (H), No. 8 (Bi), No. 9 (Li), No. 14 (K) and No. 26 (O_2). The application of the "Rabi field" to the measurement of the K atomic moment in U.z.M. No. 12 has already been mentioned. The first attempt to measure "small" moments of the order of 1/1000 Bohr magneton, which may result from the rotation of heavy particles (protons) or from intrinsic nuclear moments, was reported in U.z.M. No. 3, but the observations on beams of H_2O molecules deflected in a modified Stern-Gerlach field of an inhomogeneity of the order of 10^6 gauss/cm were only of a qualitative nature and did no more than demonstrate the feasibility of using the molecular beam method for the detection of magnetic moments of this order of magnitude.

The subject remained dormant until 1932, when improvements in technique permitted a more promising attack on this problem. The U.z.M. Nos. 24, 27, and 29 give account of a series of measurements with a (for that period) remarkable accuracy of 10% of the magnetic moment of the proton,* the rotational magnetic moment of the H_2 molecule and an estimate of the magnetic moment of the deuteron. All three values turned out to be quite different from the theoretical predictions, a probably well-known fact, but worth mentioning as an illustration for the need to obtain experimental verification for even apparently "sure" theories. This is also an appropriate place to refer to the subsequent brilliant work on nuclear moments by Rabi and his students of which examples are given in this volume.

Regarding the third item on the "Program", I am not aware of any successful work during the Hamburg period, but in later research at Columbia and elsewhere, the molecular beam method has been successfully applied to the measurement of quadrupole and octopole moments.

The next problem, electric dipole moments, was attacked at a rather early stage. U.z.M. No. 7 describes experiments leading to an order-of-magnitude determination of the electric dipole moments of binary salts, e.g. KCl, and U.z.M. No. 19 to the measurement of the moment of p-nitraniline. Other measurements of moments of organic molecules were reported outside of the U.z.M. series,[6] but really accurate measurements were only performed later at Columbia with the resonance method. The same applies to item 5 of the "Program".

Regarding point 6, the Hamburg period can account only for a beginning in U.z.M. No. 20. The problem has been more extensively investigated at various places later.

Point 7 has been investigated and verified in U.z.M. No. 30, but I am not aware of any later experiments concerning this subject.

In contrast, point 8 has received a great deal of attention. Probably

* This work was specifically referred to in Stern's Nobel Prize Citation.

the most accurate measurements of the Hamburg period were made in this area, and I am not aware of any subsequent work improving on these measurements, although the subject cannot by any standards be considered to have been exhausted by these experiments. In U.z.M. No. 15 the basic diffraction experiments with He and H_2 beams on crystal surfaces (LiF) and the theory of diffraction from crossed gratings are presented with great detail. The dependence of the de Broglie wavelength on the mass and velocity (temperature) of the beam molecules was tested over a wide range and the effective grating constant of the lattice was found to be the distance between ions of the same sign, not the crystallographic lattice constant. In U.z.M. No. 18, the diffraction experiments with He beams from LiF surfaces were refined by the use of monoenergetic beams in order to obtain sharper diffraction patterns. Monochromization was obtained in two ways, either by a "spectroscopic" method, i.e. by diffraction from a crystal and selection of atoms within a narrow range of diffraction angle, or by a procedure analogous to the Fizeau arrangement for the measurement of the velocity of light, consisting of two toothed wheels rotating with a fixed phase difference at various angular velocities so as to permit only atoms of certain velocity ranges to pass.* In both cases, the monoenergetic beams were analyzed with respect to their de Broglie wavelength (velocity) by a LiF crystal surface. The second method allowed a verification of the de Broglie relation $\lambda = h/mv$, where v was measured by purely mechanical means and λ computed from the diffraction angle and the lattice constant, with an accuracy of about 1%.

The foregoing paragraphs contain the extent of the realization of the 1926 "Program" during the Hamburg period. It is not surprising that a few other subjects were taken up which were not anticipated in 1926. Among them are the investigations of the reflection of molecular beams from surfaces, which are, of course, strongly related to the diffraction experiments. In U.z.M. No. 10, specular reflection of He and H_2 beams on glass and metal surfaces at small glancing angles of incidence was first observed; in U.z.M. No. 21 the reflection of Hg atoms from NaCl and LiF surfaces was investigated, and U.z.M. Nos. 23 and 25 deal with the finer details of the reflection and diffraction of molecular beams; (these papers could just as well be listed under point 8 of the "Program"). Another paper, U.z.M. No. 16, deals with the utilization of the different magnetic properties of monoatomic and diatomic molecules of alkali metals for the determination of the dissociation constant

---

* This procedure, in a less refined form, has been used in U.z.M. No. 13 for a verification of the Maxwellian distribution law of velocities. A later, much more elaborate version of this method is described in paper No. 3 of this volume.

and the heat of dissociation of these molecules by deflection of beams consisting of monomers and dimers as a function of the source temperature.

Finally, a subject marking the beginning of a new and powerful technique is contained in U.z.M. Nos. 17 and 22. This is the reorientation of space quantized atoms passing abruptly from a magnetic field of a certain direction to one of a different direction, colloquially known as "flopping" in the later literature. It is this effect which was so brilliantly exploited by Rabi for the development of the molecular beam resonance method which made possible measurements of an accuracy rivalling the most accurate physical measurements.

In the summer of 1933, the molecular beam work in Hamburg came to an abrupt end. Stern and the author went to Carnegie Institute of Technology and began to rebuild a laboratory. Starting on a small scale, they concentrated first on refining the measurements of the nuclear magnetic moments of the proton and deuteron. Later other subjects were taken up, but the momentum of the Hamburg laboratory was never regained. With the outbreak of the war, research shifted to other problems. Stern retired in 1945, and the author left in 1950. A small program is still in operation, devoted at present to the detailed study of the interaction of molecules with solid surfaces. (See paper No. 3 of this volume.)

In the meantime, the laboratory at Columbia University, started by Rabi after his return from Hamburg in 1929, had become the focal point of molecular beam research. An example of the current work there is paper No. 5 of this volume, but the authors of papers Nos. 2, 4, 6, and 7 also received their introduction to molecular beams at Columbia. The influence of Stern's work can be recognized throughout.

A few words will be said about the last paper. This is reprinted from the *Physical Review*, with the permission of the editor, for the following reasons: First, it contains a direct application of the procedure used in U.z.M. No. 27. Secondly, the desirability of performing such an experiment was discussed by Stern as soon as neutron beams became available, but it could not be carried out except at a National Laboratory possessing a pile with a sufficiently large thermal neutron flux. Dealing no longer with molecular beams in the conventional sense, it has been included as an example for the broad influence of Stern's thinking beyond the scope of his original program.

The last year has finally given proof to the theorem that even the purest research leads ultimately to practical applications. I am sure that Stern never expected to see a molecular beam device in a commercial catalog. But now a cesium beam clock, guaranteed to be accurate to one part in 10^{10}, and thus exceeding the accuracy of all other time measuring devices, can be purchased ready for use. It is suggested as an interesting speculation to contemplate the effects of a molecular beam industry on the future of molecular beam research.

REFERENCES

(a) THE U.z.M. SERIES (all in *Zeitschrift für Physik*).

U.z.M. No. 1.   O. Stern, Vol. 39, 751, 1926
No. 2.   F. Knauer and O. Stern, Vol. 39, 764, 1926
No. 3.   F. Knauer and O. Stern, Vol. 39, 780, 1926
No. 4.   A. Leu, Vol. 41, 551, 1927
No. 5.   O. Stern, Vol. 41, 563, 1927
No. 6.   E. Wrede, Vol. 41, 569, 1927
No. 7.   E. Wrede, Vol. 44, 261, 1927
No. 8.   A. Leu, Vol. 49, 498, 1928
No. 9.   J. B. Taylor, Vol. 52, 846, 1929
No. 10.   F. Knauer and O. Stern, Vol. 53, 766, 1929
No. 11.   F. Knauer and O. Stern, Vol. 53, 779, 1929
No. 12.   I. I. Rabi, Vol. 54, 190, 1929
No. 13.   B. Lammert, Vol. 56, 244, 1929
No. 14.   J. B. Taylor, Vol. 57, 242, 1929
No. 15.   I. Estermann and O. Stern, Vol. 61, 95, 1930
No. 16.   L. C. Lewis, Vol. 69, 786, 1931
No. 17.   T. E. Phipps and O. Stern, Vol. 73, 185, 1931
No. 18.   I. Estermann, O. Frisch, and O. Stern, Vol. 73, 348, 1931
No. 19.   M. Wohlwill, Vol. 80, 67, 1933
No. 20.   F. Knauer, Vol. 80, 80, 1933
No. 21.   B. Josephy, Vol. 80, 755, 1933
No. 22.   R. Frisch and E. Segrè, Vol. 80, 610, 1933
No. 23.   R. Frisch and O. Stern, Vol. 84, 430, 1933
No. 24.   R. Frisch and O. Stern, Vol. 45, 4, 1933
No. 25.   R. Frisch, Vol. 84, 443, 1933
No. 26.   R. Schnurmann, Vol. 85, 212, 1933
No. 27.   I. Estermann and O. Stern, Vol. 85, 17, 1933
No. 28.   I. Estermann and O. Stern, Vol. 85, 135, 1933
No. 29.   I. Estermann and O. Stern, Vol. 86, 132, 1933
No. 30.   R. Frisch, Vol. 86, 42, 1933

(b) OTHERS

[1] L. Dunoyer, *Le Radium* 8, 142, 1911; 10, 400, 1913.
[2] O. Stern, *Z. Phys.* 2, 49, 1920; 3, 417, 1920.
[3] O. Stern, *Z. Phys.* 7, 249, 1921; W. Gerlach and O. Stern, *Z. Phys.* 8, 110, 1921; 9, 349, 1922; 9, 353, 1922.
[4] R. Fraser, "Molecular Rays", Cambridge, 1931.
[5] I. Estermann, *Z. phys. Chem.* 106, 403, 1923; *Z. Electrochem.* 31, 441, 1925; *Z. Phys.* 33, 320, 1925; O. Brill, Dissertation, Hamburg 1929.
[6] I. Estermann, *Z. phys. Chem.* B, 1, 161, 1928; 2, 287, 1929; I. Estermann and M. Wohlwill, *Z. phys. Chem.* B, 20, 195, 1933.

2

Molecular and Atomic Beams at Berkeley

W. A. NIERENBERG

Institute for Basic Research in Science,
University of California, Berkeley, California

I. Introduction

Berkeley is now the home of Professor O. Stern, whose seventieth birthday we are commemorating. This article is a résumé of the data and results presented at the Brookhaven Conference on Molecular Beams (1957) by the present group at Berkeley on the spins and moments of radioactive nuclei of short half-lives. In this introduction it is particularly apropos to present a short history of molecular beam research at Berkeley. In this endeavor, the author is greatly indebted to Professor L. B. Loeb for much of the material. The first research at Berkeley, using molecular beams, is recorded in a master's thesis of 1926 by Arthur Stanton Adams, entitled "The Reflection of Zinc Atoms from Heated Surfaces." This early research, and the others to be described, were started under the powerful stimulus of the results from the group of workers under Professor Stern. The members of the Department of Physics at Berkeley were greatly impressed and felt that some effort in the same direction should be made. Under the direction of Professor E. E. Hall, then chairman of the department, a thesis was completed in 1927 by Newton S. Herod on "The Distribution of Velocities in Metallic Vapor". Except for the thesis, this work was never published. This same field of research was continued with an improved apparatus by Ira F. Zartman (under the direction of Professor Loeb). Zartman received his Ph.D. in 1930 and published his results in the *Phys. Rev.* **37,** 382 (1931) under the title "The Direct Measurement of Molecular Velocities." Cheng Chuan Ko received his degree in 1933 and published his results in the *J. Franklin Institute* **217,** 173 (1934) under the title "The Heat of Dissociation of Bi_2 Determined by the Method of Molecular Beams." The work of these two scientists has become somewhat of a classic due to the variety and nature of the results obtained. During this period (1929–1930), Professor Stern was visiting at Berkeley with the title of Lecturer in Physics and Chemistry. Shortly thereafter (1931–1932) Professor I. Estermann was Visiting Research Associate and conducted research as an International Fellow of the Rockefeller Foundation. Despite the limited time available, a molecular beam apparatus was constructed, and a measurement of the electric dipole moment of HCl was made. This was a continuation of work started at Hamburg with R. G. J. Fraser, who was then at Cambridge. The results are published in an article with R. G. J. Fraser: "The Deflection of Molecular Rays in an Electric Field: The Electric Moment of Hydrogen Chloride," *J. Chem. Phys.* **1**, 390 (1933). This apparatus used a special high-speed pump that was designed by Estermann and H. T. Byck. The work on the pump was published in *Rev. Sci. Instr.* **3**, 482 (1932) and *Phys. Rev.* **39**, 553 (1932) (A). Byck was a National Research Fellow and, in addition, was an Instructor in Physics, 1930–1933.

In December, 1932, E. M. McMillan came to Berkeley from Princeton, where he had written his Ph.D. thesis on "Deflections of Beams of HCl Molecules in a Non-Homogeneous Electric Field" under C. T. Zahn and, later, E. U. Condon. McMillan, then a National Research Fellow had proposed as a problem the determination of the proton magnetic moment. He hardly started the problem when Stern announced the measurement at Hamburg. This left McMillan undecided and he changed his field of research with some success. Because of the war and other interests, this field of research was dormant at Berkeley until 1950. About 1951, Professor H. B. Silsbee joined the physics department in order to pursue the subject. A molecular beam apparatus was built and resulted in a thesis (1953) by George Bemski on "The Fluorine Resonance in Molecular Beams".[1] At the same time, the Engineering Research Institute started research, under the aegis of Professor Estermann, on the scattering of molecules from a surface. Dr. F. Hurlbut obtained his Ph.D. in this research and is still actively connected with it. Professor Estermann is still actively associated with this research and spent the summers of 1948, 1950, and 1957 with the Institute. In 1951, the group at Berkeley began research on short-lived radioactive species. Since other groups elsewhere made excellent progress on neutron-activated isotopes, it was decided to push forward on cyclotron-induced activities. These were more difficult, owing to the low production, but offered more isotopes for study. A zero-moment apparatus was started in 1951, and J. P. Hobson and J. C. Hubbs wrote their doctoral theses[2] in 1953 on the spin and moment of 4.8 hr Rb[81]. With the special techniques developed for producing, detecting, and collecting the isotopes well in hand, the zero-moment equipment was converted to a Zacharias-Rabi "flop-in" apparatus in the fall of 1955, and the first measurements were made in February, 1956. R. J. Sunderland wrote his thesis (1956) on the radioactive rubidium isotopes,[3] and H. A. Shugart received his Ph.D. (1957) with a thesis based on the cesium isotopes.[4] Because of the special health hazards, there are now two other apparatuses operating, one primarily for transuranic elements and one for the radiohalogens. J. L. Worcester received his Ph.D. in 1957 for work on the gallium isotopes,[5] and G. O. Brink received his in 1956 for work on the thallium isotopes.[6] To date, the spins of 36 isotopes have been observed, three earlier by other groups or other methods. The hyperfine structures of approximately half of these have been determined, and most of the remainder will yield in time. Much is still to be done. In addition to new spin measurements, such parameters as the hyperfine anomalies will be measured.

The remainder of this article will be in three sections. The first section will deal with those atoms in $J = \frac{1}{2}$ ground states, such as Rb, Cs, Cu, Au, Ag, etc., for which the beam technique is essentially the same. The second section will treat those atoms which are available in quantity in both $^2P_{\frac{3}{2}}$ and $^2P_{\frac{1}{2}}$ states, such as I, Br, and Ga. The third section will be devoted to Pu^{239}, which is the first transuranic investigation to be completed by atomic beams.[7] This account cannot be complete in itself, and the reader is referred to several earlier works on specific details of the methods employed.[8]

II. The $^2S_{\frac{1}{2}}$ Ground States

There are many reasons for choosing $^2S_{\frac{1}{2}}$ atoms for initial research in this field. First, this group includes the alkalis whose beam-forming properties are known to be particularly facile and for which the normalization problem is particularly simple due to the ease in detecting the carrier isotope. Second, the intensity of a resonance line goes as $2/(2I +1)(2J +1)$ and is greatest for $J = \frac{1}{2}$ ($J = 0$ is, of course, excluded), where I is the nuclear spin and J is the electronic angular momentum. Third, the relative simplicity of the Hamiltonian for $J = \frac{1}{2}$ makes the problem of determining the $\Delta \nu$ (hyperfine separation) easier and reduces the difficulty encountered with multiple quantum transitions. Fourth, for these states, $g_J \cong -2$, thus leading to a large deflection for the "flop-in" states.[8,9] It is not surprising, therefore, that most radioactive spin determinations have been done for these atoms. Obviously, it is not possible to treat in detail all twenty-five radioactive spins that have been observed on $J = \frac{1}{2}$ atoms in Berkeley. Therefore, the discussion will be limited to the six isotopes of gold, Au^{191}, Au^{192}, Au^{193},

Au^{194}, Au^{196}, and Au^{198}, whose half-lives are 3 h, 4.8 h, 17 h, 39 h, 5.6 d, and 2.7 d, respectively. Results on these isotopes were presented for the first time by H. A. Shugart at the 3rd Brookhaven Conference on Atomic Beams, October 31, and November 1, 1957. (Au^{198} had previously been measured by the group at Princeton.) In addition, some discussion of the cyclotron-produced Cs isotopes will be included to illustrate some problems not encountered with the Au isotopes and to illuminate the procedure for finding $\Delta\nu$. The isotopes of Au just mentioned can be produced by bombardment of alphas on Ir or by protons or deuterons on Pt. The plethora of isotopes produced,[10] plus the similarity of half-lives for possibly coincident spins, made it desirable to have two methods of producing the isotopes for possible differential determinations. There are two stable isotopes of iridium, Ir^{191} (38.5%) and Ir^{193} (61.5%). Platinum has six stable isotopes, but only four are in appreciable abundance for Au production purposes. They are Pt^{194} (33%), Pt^{195} (34%), Pt^{196} (25%), and Pt^{198} (7%). The various isotopes have been produced as follows.

Au^{191}: $(\alpha, 4n)$ on Ir^{191}.

Au^{192}: $(\alpha, 3n)$ on Ir^{191}.

Au^{193}: $(\alpha, 2n)$ on Ir^{191}, and $(\alpha, 4n)$ on Ir^{193}.

Au^{194}: (α, n) on Ir^{191}, $(\alpha, 3n)$ on Ir^{193}, and (p, n) on Pt^{194}.

Au^{195}: (p, n) on Pt^{195}, and $(\alpha, 2n)$ on Ir^{193} (the latter was not observed in these experiments).

Au^{196} (14 h): (α, n) on Ir^{193} and (p, n) on Pt^{196} (this isotope was not observed in these experiments, and it is problematical whether any appreciable quantity was made).

Au^{196} (5.6 d): $(d, 2n)$ on Pt^{196}, and (α, n) on Ir^{193} (the latter was not observed in these experiments).

Au^{198} (2.7 d): (p, n) on Pt^{198} and $(d, 2n)$ on Pt^{198}.

From the very first run, resonances corresponding to approximately the correct number were observed but, because of near coincidences, it was necessary to analyze the decay of the resonance very carefully to ascertain the degree of enrichment of the appropriate isotopes. No chemistry is reasonably possible with Ir as the target material, since it is extremely difficult to put into solution. Fortunately this is a situation where the Au can be directly evaporated from the Ir. The Ir foil is precut, before bombardment, into pieces sufficiently small to fit an atomic beam oven. The oven is heated to a temperature below the melting point of Ir, and a very steady, useful beam of Au ensues. In one run the beam was held reasonably constant for eight hours, and the Ir was in condition to be reused for bombardment. The beam itself was collected on sulfur-coated buttons and counted on the now conventional x-ray counters.[3] The normalization of the beam was accomplished by taking samples regularly with the stop-wire removed. Similarly it was possible to evaporate the Au from the Pt targets, and several measurements were made in this manner. However, the beam was decidedly unsteady, and most of the runs were undertaken with samples that were chemically separated by the standard technique using ethyl acetate. A brief description of the recipe used is as follows. The Pt target is dissolved in aqua regia, and carrier Au is added in the amount necessary to obtain a beam of given intensity for the needed running time. The solution is boiled to dryness and redissolved in 6N HCl. Ethyl acetate is added, the $AuCl_3$ goes immediately to the ethyl acetate phase, and the HCl is drawn off from the bottom. The ethyl acetate is evaporated, the residue is redissolved in 3N HCl, and the Au is reduced by bubbling SO_2 through the solution. The gold is separated by centrifugation or coagulation by boiling, and the solid gold is transferred to the oven which is made of Ta. The oven is heated by electron bombardment until a beam of about 100 counts per minute per minute of exposure is obtained.

The resonance field is calibrated with a Rb beam from a permanently situated oven. The Au oven can be moved to one side for field calibration and returned for beam work. One major difficulty that occurred was the abnormally wide variations in $\Delta\nu$ for the various Au isotopes. The $\Delta\nu$ of Au^{198} is about 22,000 Mc/sec, and that of Au^{192} (4.8 h) is about 400 Mc/sec, with the other isotopes more or less uniformly distributed between these limits. In fact, the Au^{192} moment is 0.008 nuclear magnetons, which is very small. This means that quadratic shifts from the Zeeman frequencies occur more readily; great care has to be exercised in choosing C-field values and more complete resonance curves are required than is usually the case in spin determinations. The beam collection for Au is fortunately simple, since the standard sulfur surfaces work very well. (The halogens, however, offer great difficulty and, finally, freshly evaporated Ag surfaces were decided on as being the most reliable and efficient of all the ones tried.)

Figure 1 is an example of a full beam compared to the decays of resonances observed for spin 1 and spin $\frac{3}{2}$ for Au. The assignments are made by decay. Fig. 2 is an example of the $I = 1$ resonance, showing the two components of the spin. The 4.8 h Au^{192} has a large quadratic shift and has been shifted away from the resonance. Fig. 3 is a resonance of the $I = 1$, counted at different times, showing the two components. Fig. 4 is a resonance of the 17.5 h component $(I = \frac{3}{2})$. This data and other similar runs yielded the values for the Au isotopes given in the table at the end of the article.

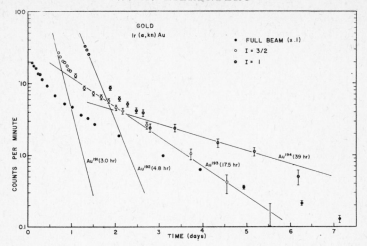

Fig. 1. The decay of two resonances observed in an experiment on Au isotopes. The resonances correspond to $I = 1$, and $I = \frac{3}{2}$.

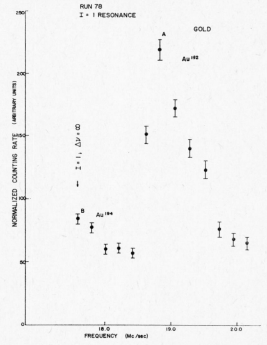

Fig. 2. A sweep of the spin $I = 1$ region showing the two spin components. Point B decayed with a pure 39 h half-life; point A decayed with a 4.8 h half-life. The Au^{192} shows a large quadratic shift at this low field.

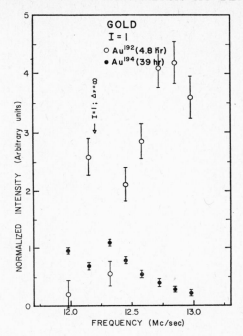

Fig. 3. $I = 1$ resonance curve, analytically resolved into two components of 4.8 h and 39 h half-lives. The Au[192] shows a large quadratic shift due to its small magnetic moment.

The research on the Cs isotopes, although similar in many ways to that on the Au, is sufficiently different in detail to warrant an abbreviated account emphasizing these differences. The isotopes studied in some detail were Cs[127], Cs[129], Cs[130], and Cs[132]. In addition, the Cs[131] spin was remeasured. There is only one stable isotope of I, namely I[127]. The (α, kn) reaction was used on BaI$_2$ to make Cs[127] (6.2 h), Cs[129] (31 h), and Cs[130] (30 m). The (p, n) reaction was employed on gaseous Xe to make Cs[129], Cs[131], and Cs[132]. The isotopes of Xe involved are Xe[129] (29%), Xe[131] (21%), and Xe[132] (27%), respectively. The chemistry used with the BaI$_2$ target is very interesting and exemplifies the special problems of this research. If CsI were used for the target, there would be too much carrier for the maximum allowed running time of the beam. Furthermore, the BaI$_2$ is more stable and packs more I atoms into the given range of the alpha particles. The chemistry then consists in dissolving the BaI$_2$ in water with the required amount of CsI carrier and precipitating the Ba with ammonium carbonate. The NH$_4$I and $(NH_4)_2CO_3$ are differentially sublimed and the CsI residue is redissolved in a few drops of water and transferred into and dried in the oven, which is made of iron. Ca is then added, and the usual Cs beam is produced. The Xe is in a special target about 40 cm long and 5 × 10 cm in cross section which has a thin aluminium window at one end. After bombardment, the Xe is frozen out onto a liquid N_2 trap, and a controlled amount of water with carrier CsI is sucked in, after which the whole assembly is agitated. The residue is reduced in

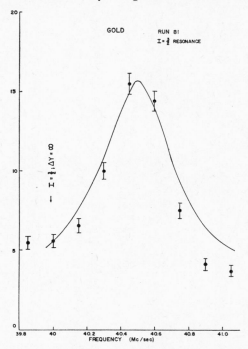

Fig. 4. A simple resonance of the 17.5 h (Au^{193}) component.

volume and transferred and dried into the oven as before. The (α, kn) research was first done at a time when the 30 m Cs^{130} was gone. Only one resonance was observed and that was for a spin of $\frac{1}{2}$. For equivalent exposures the initial counting rate on the spin $\frac{1}{2}$ resonance was 100 ± 1.5 and on all other resonance buttons, averaged in arbitrary units, 1.5. This is a typical signal-to-noise ratio for spin $\frac{1}{2}$. Fig. 5 is the decay of the spin $\frac{1}{2}$ sample and that of the full beam sample. They are quite similar, and the inference is that both components have the same spin. Fig. 6 is the decay of another run where the isotopes are produced by a thinner target to enhance the $(\alpha, 4n)$ reaction. Both the resonance decay and the main beam decay show the same relative increase in the

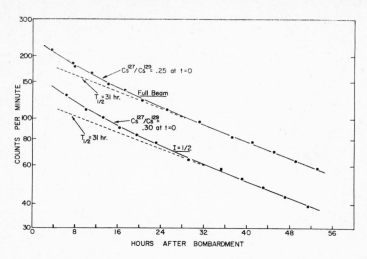

Fig. 5. The radioactive decay of a straight-through beam sample and an $I = \frac{1}{2}$ resonance sample. This was the only spin sample that showed an appreciable counting rate. Both curves are alike within experimental error, indicating that Cs127 and Cs129 both have $I = \frac{1}{2}$.

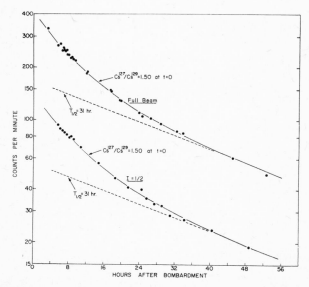

Fig. 6. Same as Fig. 5. The isotopes are produced by bombardment on a thin sample. The $(\alpha, 4n)$ reaction is clearly enhanced relative to the $(\alpha, 2n)$ reaction. Both curves are still parallel, indicating that both isotopes have $I = \frac{1}{2}$.

fast component. In order to measure the spin of the 30 m Cs¹³⁰, a short bombardment was obtained and the same chemistry performed. It was done very quickly and inefficiently, however. The signal on spin 1 was 100 ± 13, compared to an average of about 10 ± 5 on spins 0, 2, 3, and 4, in each of two runs. The signal-to-noise ratio was sufficiently good that it was possible to carry the resonance to high enough fields to measure the $\Delta\nu$ and, therefore, the nuclear magnetic moment, despite the short half-life of the material. Fig. 7 shows the decay of the full beam compared to that of the resonance.

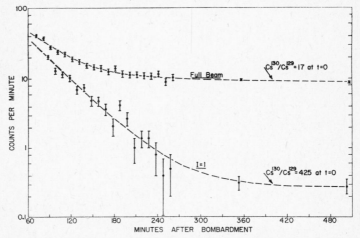

Fig. 7. The radioactive decay of a spin 1 sample. The isotope separation is clear and the $I = 1$ must be assigned to 30 m Cs¹³⁰.

Figure 8 is the result of a resonance search of a run on the (p, n) reaction on Xe. Three clear resonances were observed, and they decayed with half-lives appropriate to Cs¹²⁹, Cs¹³¹, and Cs¹³². The corresponding spins are $\frac{1}{2}$, $\frac{5}{2}$, and 2. The full beam decay is composite compared to the excellent straight lines of the three resonances. This isotope separation alone is independent confirmation of the resonances, as well as that afforded by the intensity factors. It is very gratifying to obtain agreement on the Cs¹²⁹ spin after production by two independent means. It is also gratifying to check the Cs¹³¹ by an independent production and detection scheme. Originally the spin of Cs¹³¹ was detected mass-spectroscopically.[11]

The $\Delta\nu$'s of these isotopes were determined by direct application of the Breit-Rabi formula to the flop-in transition. They are too large for a search for the $\Delta F = \pm 1$ transition at the precision required or attainable. In all cases the Fermi-Segrè formula was used to calculate the

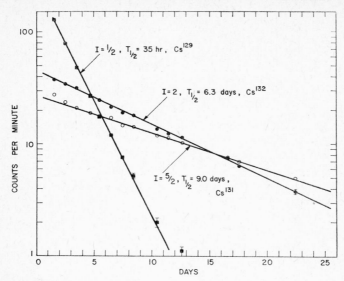

Fig. 8. Spin $\frac{1}{2}$, 2, and $\frac{5}{2}$ resonances in the (p, n) on Xe reaction. The background effect is so low that each decay curve is a straight line.

ratio of the g_I of the unknown to the g_I of the comparing isotope, given the respective $\Delta\nu$'s. The two equations are

$$\Delta\nu = \frac{[\nu + (\mu_0 g_I H/h)][(-\mu_0 g_J H/h) - \nu]}{\nu + [\mu_0 g_J H/h(2I+1)] + [2I\mu_0 g_I H/h(2I+1)]}, \tag{1}$$

and

$$|g_I| \cong \frac{\Delta\nu(2I_1+1)}{\Delta\nu_1(2I+1)}|g_{I_1}|. \tag{2}$$

The latter relation is good to better than 1% for Cs, and the subscripted quantities refer to Cs^{133} for which they are well known. Both formulas can be combined into a very useful form.

$$\Delta\nu = \frac{2C}{B + (B^2 - 4AC)^{\frac{1}{2}}}, \tag{3a}$$

where

$$A = \frac{2I\mu_0 H(2I_1+1)g_{I_1}}{h\Delta\nu_1(2I+1)^2}, \tag{3b}$$

$$B = v + \frac{\mu_0 g_J H}{h(2I+1)} + \frac{\mu_0 H(2I_1+1)g_{I_1}}{h\Delta v_1(2I+1)}\left(\frac{\mu_0 g_J H}{h}+v\right), \tag{3c}$$

and

$$C = v[(\mu_0 g_J H/h)+v]. \tag{3d}$$

This unusual form of the solution to the quadratic equation is needed to prevent loss of significant figures in the final answer for Δv due to the smallness of A. Fig. 9 is a resonance fit by least squares analysis to a typical Cs^{132} resonance. Fig. 10 shows the method used to determine the sign of g_I. Δv is computed for each resonance, assuming first that $g_I > 0$, and second that $g_I < 0$. The two values are denoted by Δv^+ and Δv^-. Both values are plotted versus H and the set of Δv's belonging to the ultimately correct sign of g_I will fall along a horizontal line, while the set belonging to the incorrect sign of g_I will fall along a theoretically predictable curve. Since $g_I > 0$ for Cs^{132}, the data shows a very good fit under these assumptions.

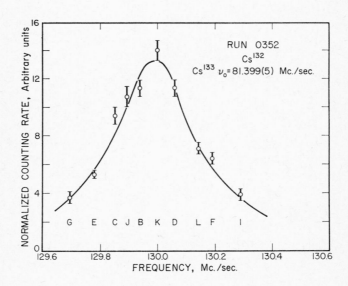

Fig. 9. A resonance curve of Cs^{132} with Cs^{133} as the calibrating substance. The curve is a least squares fit. The uncertainty in the position of the resonance center due to counting statistics is much less than the half to one-quarter line width uncertainty that is used for calculating Δv.

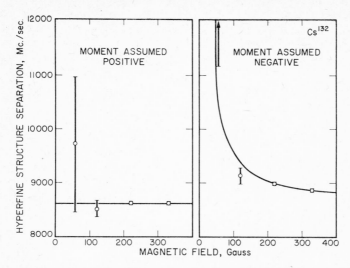

Fig. 10. Consistency test for determining the sign of g_I. Cs^{132} is the substance. The graph on the left displays the $\Delta\nu$'s obtained from measurements at different fields, assuming $g_I > 0$. The values fit a horizontal straight line. The graph on the right shows the $\Delta\nu$'s calculated for $g_I < 0$ along with the theoretical solid line which assumes that the assignment $g_I < 0$ is incorrect. The conclusion is that $g_I > 0$.

III. The $^2P_{\frac{3}{2}}$ Atoms[12]

The gallium, bromine, and iodine isotopes fall into this category of atoms that can be studied in the $^2P_{\frac{3}{2}}$ state. The isotopes that have been successfully studied at Berkeley are Ga^{66}, Ga^{67}, Ga^{68}, Br^{82}, I^{123}, I^{124}, and I^{131}, whose half-lives are 9.4 h, 78 h, 68 m, 36 h, 13 h, 4.5 d, and 8.1 d, respectively. All are cyclotron-produced, except the Br^{82} and I^{131}. The first is produced by (n, γ) pile reactions; the second is produced as a fission product. The Ga isotopes were produced by (α, kn) reactions on Cu^{63} (69%) and Cu^{65} (31%) on the Crocker 60-in. cyclotron.[13] Attempts to distill the Ga directly out of the Cu target, a method which succeeded with Au out of Ir, Ag out of Rh, and Cu out of Co, failed completely. Plating the Ga on Pt foils, which were crumpled into an oven, also failed to yield a beam. The only success was achieved with a chemistry that resulted in pure Ga in a carbon oven. Ovens of other materials, such as Fe and Ta, failed. The final procedure involved the plating of the radiogallium and carrier onto a 0.004-in. Pt wire, which protruded $\frac{1}{8}$ in. from a pyrex tube. The Ga will often coalesce into globules, particularly under the influence of a warm, dilute

HCl bath. The globule can be shaken off into the carbon oven or scraped directly in. Any Cu that passes the chemistry complicates the procedure and an abbreviated description is as follows. The Cu target is dissolved in about 15 cc of 10N HNO_3 with the carrier Ga, and the solution is boiled to reduce the volume. About 60 cc of 6N HCl saturated with ether and 50 cc of ethyl ether are added, and the gallium chloride is ether-extracted. The ether is washed several additional times with 6N HCl to remove the last traces of the Cu. The $GaCl_3$ is extracted with 15 cc of H_2O, and NaOH is added until the Ga precipitates as $Ga(OH)_3$. The $Ga(OH)_3$ is centrifuged and redissolved in the smallest possible amount of concentrated NaOH; then two platinum electrodes are introduced, and the plating can commence as described above. In 15 minutes about 50% of the activity is recovered. The plating then slows down, and 75% in one hour was considered good efficiency.

The Br^{82} was produced by (n, γ) on Br^{81} (49%). I^{123} and I^{124} are produced[14] by (α, kn) reactions on Sb^{121} (57%) and Sb^{123} (43%). Chemistry was required in all cases, and it turned out to be unexpectedly difficult. It was necessary to prepare the halogen in gaseous form so that it could enter the discharge tube at a carefully regulated rate. The discharge tube turned out to be singularly efficient. When operating properly, the Stern-Gerlach fields of the apparatus threw out more than 95% of the beam, indicating that only a small fraction of the diatomic molecules were left in the $^1\Sigma_0$ state. If it is assumed that the deflected component is atomic, then an efficiency of about 95% in atom-making is indicated. Fig. 11 is a drawing of the discharge tube and underneath is a circuit diagram of the regulator. The apparatus is somewhat novel in that it is an "inside out" apparatus. All magnets and windings are completely outside the vacuum. Fig. 12 is a perspective drawing of the apparatus. For safety reasons a glove box surrounds the source end of the apparatus. In all of these experiments, as with the Au isotopes, an auxiliary alkali oven is maintained for field calibration. All of the apparatuses in Berkeley, except one, are of the asymmetric type, in that the A-focusing field is very small compared to the B-focusing field.

The I^{131} comes in the form of NaI from Oak Ridge. Iodine is precipitated by the addition of $NaNO_2$ and H_2SO_4 and the iodine extracted into CS_2. 200 to 300 mg of I_2 are added to the solvent and the CS_2 is evaporated off under vacuum. The I^{123} and I^{124} are obtained by first dissolving the Sb metal in concentrated HCl with a few drops of H_2O_2 and a few mg of NaI carrier. The solution is neutralized with NaOH and the heavy precipitate of SbOCl filtered off; the I is again precipitated

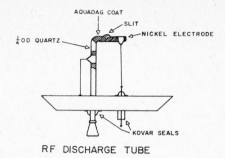

RF DISCHARGE TUBE

DISCHARGE STABILIZER

Fig. 11. The schematic of a simple discharge tube for dissociating the halogens. The circuit shown is an excellent regulator for the discharge.

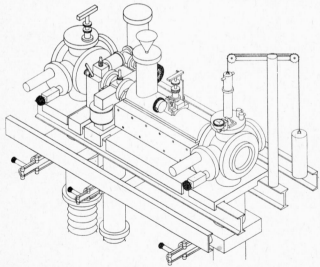

Fig. 12. A perspective view of the halogen apparatus. It is "inside out" in that the magnets and windings are all outside the vacuum. It is hoped that the radioactive cleanup problem will be less serious with this apparatus.

and extracted from the filtrate by the technique used above. The procedure for Br is different. Br^{82} is obtained in the form of KBr powder.[6] The Br is liberated by heating the KBr with concentrated H_2SO_4 and MnO_2. The Br_2 is carried over to a liquid-nitrogen-cooled flask with a stream of He. The Br is subsequently evaporated under vacuum to another nitrogen-cooled flask containing P_2O_5 and thence to a third flask which is used as an oven vial. Br^{76} and Br^{77} are obtained by dissolving the As in Caro's acid with the required amount of Br carrier. The procedure then follows as above. In all cases the flask containing the liquid or solid is attached directly to the source. The higher vapor pressure of Br necessitates the inclusion of a slow leak.

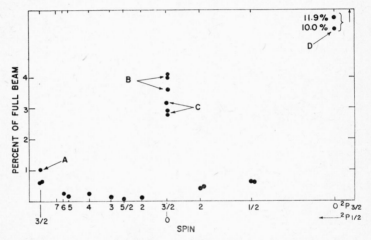

Fig. 13. Spin search involving Ga^{66} and Ga^{67}. The points at D correspond to $I = 0$, $^2P_{3/2}$. They are about 10% of the full beam. (Fig. 16 is the decay of one of these points.) The points B are the f^+ and f^- of $^2P_{3/2}$, $I = \frac{3}{2}$, which are accidentally together at low fields. The points C are the $I = 0$, $^2P_{1/2}$, points. B and C were resolved from the resonance by decay analysis (Fig. 15). The point A is $^2P_{1/2}$, $I = \frac{3}{2}$, it is above background and is resolvable by decay analysis.

Figure 13 is a survey of several spin searches for Ga^{66} and Ga^{67}; $^2P_{3/2}$ and $^2P_{1/2}$ resonances are shown for both isotopes. Fig. 14 is a decay of the main beam sample and a spin $\frac{3}{2}$ sample. Fig. 15 is a decay of the spin 0 sample for Ga^{66}. Fig. 16 is an example of a $\frac{3}{2}$ resonance at a field where the quadratic shift for the two components just begins to separate the two transitions that have a common g_F. Figs. 17 and 18a,b are similar displays of spin searches for I^{123} and I^{124}, and an I^{131} resonance; and Fig. 19 is an example of a resonance seen in I^{123} (f^- transition) showing a quadratic shift.

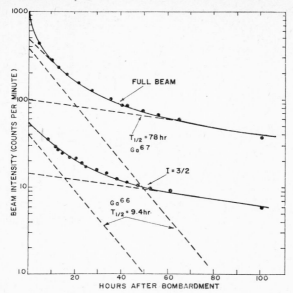

Fig. 14. The decay of a normal beam sample and the decay of the resonances B and C of Fig. 13. Both components are present as they should be, approximately the same as in the full beam. The $^2P_{\frac{1}{2}}$, $I = 0$, and $^2P_{\frac{3}{2}}$, $I = \frac{3}{2}$, resonance conditions are accidentally the same.

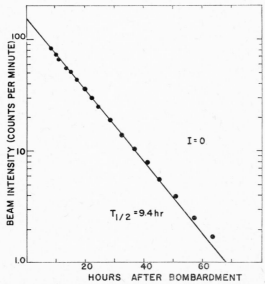

Fig. 15. The decay of a resonance from the D group of Fig. 13. It is pure Ga^{66} as it should be.

c

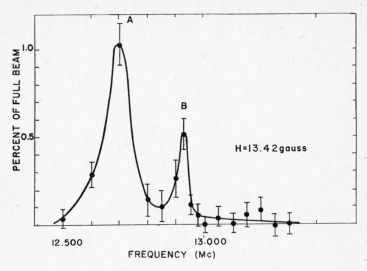

Fig. 16.   The decay of a $^2P_{\frac{3}{2}}$, $I = \frac{3}{2}$, resonance (like B of Fig. 13) at a field where the quadratic splitting is appreciable compared to the line widths. The f^+ and f^- levels, which had previously been together, are now just split.

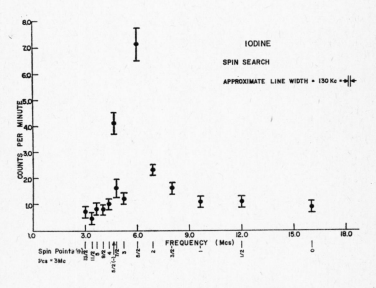

Fig. 17. Spin search for I^{123} and I^{123}.

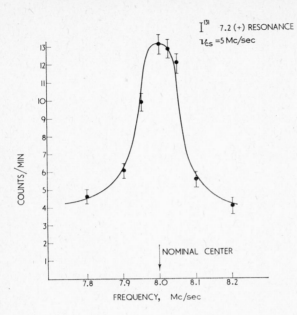

Fig. 18a. Resonance (f^+) for I^{131}.

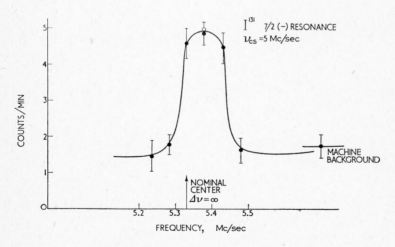

Fig. 18b. Resonance (f^-) for I^{131}.

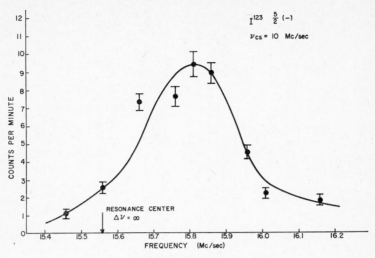

Fig. 19. Quadratic Shift in I^{123} (f^-).

The Hamiltonian, in units of $\sec^{-1}$, used to analyze results on Ga and the halogens is

$$H = a\mathbf{I}\cdot\mathbf{J} + \frac{b}{2I(2I-1)J(2J-1)}[3(\mathbf{I}\cdot\mathbf{J})^2 + \tfrac{3}{2}(\mathbf{I}\cdot\mathbf{J}) - I(I+1)J(J+1)] -$$

$$-\frac{g_J\mu_0\mathbf{J}\cdot\mathbf{H}}{h} - \frac{g_I\mu_0\mathbf{I}\cdot\mathbf{H}}{h}. \tag{4}$$

a is the magnetic dipole interaction in $\sec^{-1}$; b is the quadrupole inter-action constant in $\sec^{-1}$; μ_0 is the Bohr magneton; g_J is the atomic ground state g-factor and is approximtely $-\tfrac{4}{3}$, although the best avail-able precise value is actually used for each isotope; g_I is the nuclear g-factor and is of order 1/2000. The octupole term is not included. It is presumed to be too small for the sensitivity obtained so far with radioactive species. Fig. 20 is the Breit-Rabi diagram for $I = \tfrac{3}{2}$, where the levels are shown for $a > 0$ and $|b|$ sufficiently small so that the zero-field order is normal; the highest F level is highest in energy and the remaining F levels are in the order of decreasing F. For this case, there are just two "flop-in" transitions that are observable. Under some circumstances (relative values of b/a), the order level in zero magnetic field can be seriously changed from the above arrangement, and it is sometimes possible to observe three "flop-in" transitions. The order of

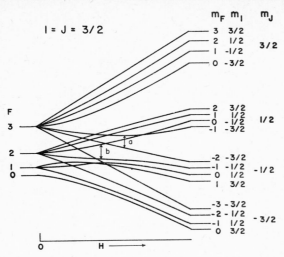

Fig. 20. The Breit-Rabi diagram for $I = \frac{3}{2}$, $J = \frac{3}{2}$. The frequencies "*a*" and "*b*" are the normally observed "flop-in" transitions. Another one is possible if the order level is changed due to a large quadrupole-dipole moment coupling ratio.

the levels depends upon the magnitude and sign of the quantity $\xi = b/a$. Tables 1 and 2 are reasonably concise statements of these level arrangements versus the quantity ξ.

TABLE 1

THE ORDER OF THE ZERO FIELD LEVELS AS A FUNCTION OF b/a. $I > 1$.

$-\infty$ $\downarrow$	$-\dfrac{4I(2I-1)}{2I-3}$ $\downarrow$	$-2I$ $\downarrow$	$\dfrac{2I(2I-1)}{2I+3}$ $\downarrow$	$\dfrac{4I(2I-1)}{2I+5}$ $\downarrow$	$\dfrac{2I(2I-1)}{3}$ $\downarrow$	$2I(2I-1)$ $\downarrow$	∞ $\downarrow$
$\frac{1}{2}$		$\frac{1}{2}$	$\frac{3}{2}$	$\frac{3}{2}$	$\frac{3}{2}$	$\frac{3}{2}$	$-\frac{3}{2}$
$-\frac{1}{2}$		$\frac{3}{2}$	$\frac{1}{2}$	$\frac{1}{2}$	$-\frac{3}{2}$	$-\frac{3}{2}$	$\frac{3}{2}$
$\frac{3}{2}$		$-\frac{1}{2}$	$-\frac{1}{2}$	$-\frac{3}{2}$	$\frac{1}{2}$	$-\frac{1}{2}$	$-\frac{1}{2}$
$-\frac{3}{2}$		$-\frac{3}{2}$	$-\frac{3}{2}$	$-\frac{1}{2}$	$-\frac{1}{2}$	$\frac{1}{2}$	$\frac{1}{2}$

The headings are functions of I for $J = \frac{3}{2}$. The columns are values of i, where $I + i$ and the vertical order indicates the arrangement of F levels in energy in zero fields. If ξ has a value between any two adjacent headings, the order of levels is given as indicated in the column between these headings, where the number in the table is to be added to I to give F. If $a > 0$, the given upper F value lies highest, if $a < 0$, the given upper F value lies lowest. If $I = \frac{3}{2}$, the most left-hand arrangement does not appear. If $I = 1$, this table does not apply.

TABLE 2

THE ORDER OF THE ZERO FIELD LEVELS AS A FUNCTION OF b/a. $I = 1$.

$-\infty$	$\downarrow$	-2	$\downarrow$	$\frac{2}{3}$	$\downarrow$	4	$\downarrow$	∞
			$\frac{5}{2}$		$\frac{5}{2}$		$\frac{1}{2}$	
			$\frac{3}{2}$		$\frac{1}{2}$		$\frac{5}{2}$	
	$\frac{1}{2}$		$\frac{1}{2}$		$\frac{3}{2}$		$\frac{3}{2}$	

This table is the same as Table 1 but for $I = 1$. The entries here are the actual F-values.

The hyperfine constants a and b have been evaluated for several of these isotopes by observing the two possible transitions for various values of the field including values that correspond to appreciable shifts of the observed resonances from the Zeeman resonance. It can be shown that, given a limited amount of material, the most conservative procedure for evaluating a and b to a given accuracy is to increase the frequency in successive steps so that at each step only about five samples are needed to cover a given frequency region. In principle only about 50 resonance points are needed to obtain the hyperfine constants to a percent or so. In practice this method works very well for $^2S_{\frac{1}{2}}$ states and usually the precision obtained is sufficient to determine the sign of g_I as well. The method is excellent for the $^2P_{\frac{3}{2}}$ states, but the difficulty in interpreting the results, to obtain the most reliable answer from the smallest amount of data is principally mathematical. First, there are two constants to be determined, a and b, and a least squares procedure is called for to fit say, 10 resonances distributed between two different lines. This is made complicated by the fact that no useful explicit formula is available, giving these frequencies as a function of a, b, and H. If the frequency of the upper transition is denoted by f^+ (by upper is meant the transitions between levels of the largest F value in the normal order) and that of the lower by f^-, it is known that f^+ is the difference between a root of a secular equation of the third degree and one of the second, and f^- is the difference between a root of a secular equation of the fourth degree and one of the third. The least square procedure[15] adopted is necessarily a trial and error procedure which converges most rapidly to the correct values of a and b and gives the errors in a and b as well as the weighted sum of the squares of the residuals. The last part, when divided by $n-2$ where n is the number of observations, is useful in determining the sign of g_I by consistency. This procedure will be described later and it will be seen that it involves the calculation of the energy levels with respect to a, b, and H and all the derivatives of these levels with respect to these parameters up to the second degree. A numerical procedure is therefore needed for calculating these quantities. Furthermore, these procedures should, if possible, be generaliz-

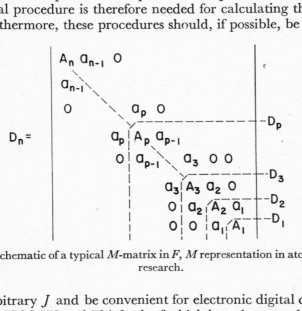

Fig. 21. Schematic of a typical M-matrix in F, M representation in atomic beam research.

able to arbitrary J and be convenient for electronic digital computers, such as the IBM 650 and 704, both of which have been used. The following method of handling the matrices seemed the most useful, and it is based on the observation that all the matrices treated in atomic beams have a uniformly simple form. If an F, M_F representation is used, the entire Hamiltonian degenerates into submatrices of constant M_F values. These matrices are Hermitian (in fact can be put into real symmetric form) and have the special property that all elements which are not on the diagonal, or not one off the diagonal, are zero. Fig. 21 is a schematic of such a matrix. Let D_n be the value of the determinant of the entire matrix, D_1 be the determinant formed by including the lower right-hand element A_1, D_2 the second-order determinant that includes A_1 and A_2 as well as the diagonal elements, etc., as shown on the figure. Then a simple recursion relation is

$$D_p = A_p D_{p-1} - |a_{p-1}|^2 D_{p-2}, \tag{5}$$

with the boundary condition that $D_0 = 1$, $D_{-1} = 0$. If x is subtracted from the diagonal matrix elements, the determinant so obtained (the indicial equation) is evaluated by the following difference equation:

$$D_p = (A_p - x)D_{p-1} - |a_{p-1}|^2 D_{p-2}, \tag{6}$$

and the derivative of the indicial equation with respect to x is

$$\frac{\partial D_p}{\partial x} = (A_p - x)\frac{\partial D_{p-1}}{\partial x} - |a_{p-1}|^2 \frac{\partial D_{p-2}}{\partial x} - D_{p-1}, \tag{7}$$

with the boundary conditions $\partial D_0/\partial x = 0$, $\partial D_{-1}/\partial x = 0$. Using Newton's method, any desired eigenvalue of the matrix can be found by choosing a close trial value and correcting with $-D_p/(\partial D_p/\partial x)$. This is iterated to the desired accuracy. Usually the zero-field root is chosen as a starting point, and successive roots are computed by incrementing H. There is no possibility of the method failing for intermediate H values because the "no M-cross rule" prevents levels in a given M_F matrix from crossing and giving double roots. Higher derivatives and derivatives with respect to other quantities obey very similar difference equations and are therefore very easily evaluated. Fortunately the problem can be put in dimensionless form as follows.

$$\frac{\mathscr{H}}{a} = \mathbf{I}\cdot\mathbf{J} + \xi Op - \frac{g_J\mu_0 H}{ha} J_z - \frac{g_I\mu_0 H}{ha} I_z ,$$

where Op is the coefficient of b in Eq. (4). If $v^+ = f^+/a$ and $v^- = f^-/a$ correspond to the dimensionless eigenvalues x_i of $\mathscr{H}/a$, such that

$$v^+ = x_1^+ - x_2^+, \tag{8}$$

$$v^- = x_1^- - x_2^-,$$

then tables of x_i can be and have been prepared at very low cost, which are universally useful. They are used by recognizing that

$$f^\pm{}_{\text{observed}} = f\pm - \frac{g_I\mu_0 H}{h}, \tag{9}$$

$$g_J \rightarrow g_J - g_I,$$

where g_J is replaced by $g_J - g_I$. The tables are computed without the g_I term for different I, ξ, and values of $g_J\mu_0 H/ha$. The indicated replacement accurately takes care of the g_I term, which is itself estimated from a by the Back-Goudsmit formula in successive approximations.

These tables are very easy to apply and are much more convenient than perturbation calculations that may have to go to as high as the sixth order for sufficient accuracy. To find the best fit we must minimize the sum

$$\sum_{+-} \sum_{i} (f_i{}^{\pm} - X_1{}^{\pm} + X_2{}^{+})^2 \, \omega_i = M, \tag{10}$$

with respect to a choice of a and b. The large X's are the small x's multiplied by a and are understood to be computed from the Hamiltonian for the given a and b and the H_i at which the measurement was taken. ω_i is the statistical weight of the measurement. The index i refers to the different measurements and the $\sum_{+-}$ refers to the possibility of two different kinds of reasonances. A trial and error procedure is called for, but it is very tricky, because each individual equation has a number of roots, only one of which is admissible. Therefore, a sufficiently good starting approximation is called for which will identify the appropriate roots (this is taken care of by the previously described tables) and a numerical method that will converge sharply and prevent oscillations into different solutions. The method used is as follows. Trial value a_n and b_n are used to compute the derivatives $\partial M/\partial a$, $\partial M/\partial b$, $\partial^2 M/\partial a^2$, $\partial^2 M/\partial b^2$, and $\partial^2 M/\partial a \partial b$ by extensions of the difference equations. The equations

$$\left(\frac{\partial^2 M}{\partial a^2}\right)_n \delta a_n + \left(\frac{\partial^2 M}{\partial a \partial b}\right)_n \delta b_n = \left(\frac{\partial M}{\partial a}\right)_n,$$

$$\left(\frac{\partial^2 M}{\partial a \partial b}\right)_n \delta a_n + \left(\frac{\partial^2 M}{\partial b^2}\right)_n \delta b_n = \left(\frac{\partial M}{\partial b}\right)_n, \tag{11}$$

are solved for δa_n and δb_n, and new trial values are obtained:

$$a_{n+1} = a_n - \delta a_n,$$

$$b_{n+1} = b_n - \delta b_n. \tag{12}$$

These are very rapidly convergent to the correct answer. If the determinant of the system (11) is denoted by Δ, the squared errors in a and b are

$$(\Delta_a)^2 = \frac{\partial^2 M/\partial b^2}{\Delta},$$

$$(\Delta_b)^2 = \frac{\partial^2 M/\partial a^2}{\Delta}. \tag{13}$$

This method was applied to both Ga^{67} and Br^{82}. The routine developed for this problem will apply, in general, to any value of I and J greater than $\frac{1}{2}$, and will accept as input information any possible transition. In the case of Ga^{67}, the results checked sixth-order perturbation calculations very nicely. Experimental points and results for Ga^{67} are given in Table 3 and Table 4.

TABLE 3

g_I ASSUMED POSITIVE. Ga^{67}

$\mu_0 H/h$	$f_{observed} + \lvert g_I \rvert \mu_0 H/h$	$f_{calculated}^{lculat} + \lvert g_I \rvert \mu_0 H/h$	Δf	Type $\pm$
18.784	12.701	12.694	$+.007$	$+$
35.535	24.274	24.278	$-.004$	$+$
50.666	34.944	34.963	$-.019$	$+$
105.581	75.541	75.552	$-.011$	$+$
152.353	112.512	112.505	$+.007$	$+$
18.784	12.938	12.944	$-.006$	$-$
35.535	25.251	25.248	$+.003$	$-$
50.666	37.139	37.140	$-.001$	$-$

$$a = 175.21 \pm .12 \text{ Mc/sec}$$

$$b = 71.97 \pm .33 \text{ Mc/sec}$$

$$\chi^2 = \Sigma \text{ weighted errors squared } = 4.2$$

All entries in the table are in megacycles per second. The calculated frequencies are arrived at assuming that g_I is positive and equal to 1.23 nuclear magnetons. The errors in a and b do not include the factor χ. The χ factor indicates about 50% probability of agreement with the functional form assumed. A similar examination must be undertaken with g_I assumed negative (Table 4). The uncertainties used as weights corresponded to ± 12.5 kc/sec for each observed frequency. This is approximately one-fifth the width of the lines at half maximum.

TABLE 4

g_I ASSUMED NEGATIVE. Ga^{67}

$\mu_0 H/h$	$f_{observed} - \lvert g_I \rvert \mu_0 H/h$	$f_{calculated} - \lvert g_I \rvert \mu_0 H/h$	Δf	Type $\pm$
18.784	12.676	12.680	$-.004$	$+$
35.535	24.227	24.249	$-.022$	$+$
50.666	34.876	34.918	$-.042$	$+$
105.581	75.400	75.429	$-.029$	$+$
152.353	112.308	112.289	$+.019$	$+$
18.784	12.913	12.927	$-.014$	$-$
35.535	25.205	25.208	$-.003$	$-$
50.666	37.071	37.069	$+.002$	$-$

$$a = 176.57 \pm .26 \text{ Mc/sec.}$$
$$b = 72.64 \pm .68 \text{ Mc/sec.}$$

The table description is the same as that for Table 3, except that the errors in a and b include the factor $\chi/\sqrt{6}$. The value of χ^2 at minimum now is 23.4. This means a probability of considerably less than 0.1% that the assumption $g_I < 0$ is correct. Combined with the conclusions from Table 3, this results in the conclusion that $g_I > 0$ for Ga^{67}.

For most of the isotopes of Ga, Br, and I investigated, the $^2P_{\frac{1}{2}}$ resonances were observed as part of the spin confirmation, but were not used for magnetic moment determinations.

IV. Pu^{239} Research[16]

To date, no new spins have been reported on the transuranic elements. Most of the initial research has gone into the chemistry of atomic beam formation. In addition, the atomic ground states and electronic g-factors are very uncertain and the first experiments are concerned with the determination of the ground state J and g_J. Fortunately the spin of Pu^{239} is known and this simplified the problem for Pu. The hyperfine constants for Pu^{239} are $I = \frac{1}{2}$, $J = 1$, $g_J = 1.4975 \pm 0.0010$, $\Delta\nu = 7.683 \pm 0.060$ Mc/sec. The research leading to a suitable Pu beam source was long and arduous, but resulted in the following successful procedure. The Pu was placed in a tungsten cup with a sharp lip. The cup was placed inside a tungsten oven but isolated from the oven by a thorium oxide barrier. In operation the oven was subjected to a strong temperature gradient from front to rear, which prevented excess flow of the liquid Pu to the slits. Fig. 22 is a sketch of the oven. The Pu beam is collected on flamed Pt foils and alpha

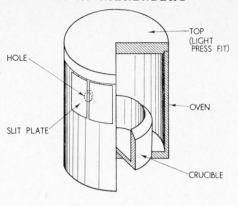

OVEN

Fig. 22. A cutaway of an oven used for the Pu^{239} research. It is made of tungsten with tantalum slits.

counting was used, since it provides great efficiency with low background.

The Hamiltonian used to analyze the experimental results is of the usual form

$$\mathcal{H} = a\mathbf{I}\cdot\mathbf{J} - g_J\mu_0\mathbf{J}\cdot\mathbf{H} - g_I\mu_0\mathbf{I}\cdot\mathbf{H}. \tag{14}$$

There are no quadrupole terms included because $I = \frac{1}{2}$. This is a simplifying feature, because the Breit-Rabi formula can be used directly with I and J interchanged to describe the energy levels.

$$\frac{W}{\Delta W} = -\frac{1}{2(2J+1)} - \frac{mg_J\mu_0H}{\Delta W} \pm \frac{1}{2}\left(1 + \frac{4mx}{2J+1} + x^2\right)^{\frac{1}{2}}. \tag{15}$$

$x = (g_J - g_I)\mu_0H/\Delta W$; $\Delta W = a(J+\frac{1}{2})$; m is the magnetic quantum number of the total angular momentum. Fig. 23 is the plot of the energy

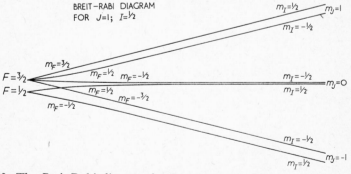

Fig. 23. The Breit-Rabi diagram for $I = \frac{1}{2}$, $J = 1$. The electronic states in strong fields, $m_J = 0$, present a difficulty in applying the "flop-in" method.

levels for $J = 1$, the case studied in greatest detail. The states $m_J = 0$ in strong field offer the complication that the simple "flop-in" technique will not work as they do for half-integral J's. At very low fields, this does not matter, because all transitions in the upper F level are easily induced at the Larmor frequency. At fields where quadratic shifts appear, application of sufficient rf current induced the double quantum transition $F = \frac{3}{2} \leftrightarrow F = \frac{3}{2}$, $M_F = \frac{1}{2} \leftrightarrow -\frac{3}{2}$, and this line was followed in detail and it fitted the Breit-Rabi formula very well. Fig. 24

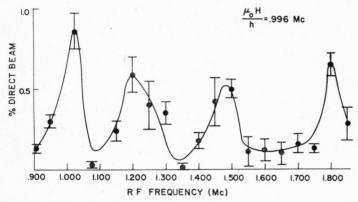

Fig. 24. Low field $\Delta F = 0$ resonances. The resonance at ~ 1 Mc/sec is $J = 1$, $F = \frac{3}{2}$; the resonance at 1.2 Mc/sec is $J = 2$, $F = \frac{3}{2}$; the resonance at 1.8 Mc/sec is $J = 2$, $F = \frac{5}{2}$; and the resonance at 1.5 Mc/sec is Pu^{238} $(I = 0)$.

is the resonance curve obtained at very low field corresponding to $\mu_0 H/h \cong 1$ Mc/sec. Four resonances are observed, one of which probably corresponds to a Pu^{240} $(I = 0)$ contaminant, one of which is $J = 1$, $F = \frac{3}{2}$, and the other two are $J = 2$, $F = \frac{3}{2}$ and $\frac{5}{2}$. This identification assumes a g_J for all states of 1.5. All F states of the $^7F_6$ multiplet are excited, but only the lowest three $(F = 0, 1, 2)$ are appreciably populated at the operating oven temperature of about 1700°C. Fig. 25 is a family of double quantum resonances $\Delta F = 0$ up to about 100 Mc/sec in frequency. Fig. 26 is a $\Delta F = 1$ transition $(\frac{3}{2} \leftrightarrow F \leftrightarrow \frac{1}{2}, \frac{1}{2} \leftrightarrow M_F \to -\frac{1}{2})$, which was used to obtain a good value of the hyperfine interval. Fig. 27 is a summary of all the double quantum transitions fitted with the results given earlier in the paper. The agreement would indicate that the assignments are correct.

It is always important to be able to evaluate the magnetic moment from the hyperfine data. In this case there have been no measurements made on any of the Pu isotopes, so the only procedure open is the direct calculation of $\langle 1/r^3 \rangle$ for the atom. This is never very satisfactory, but

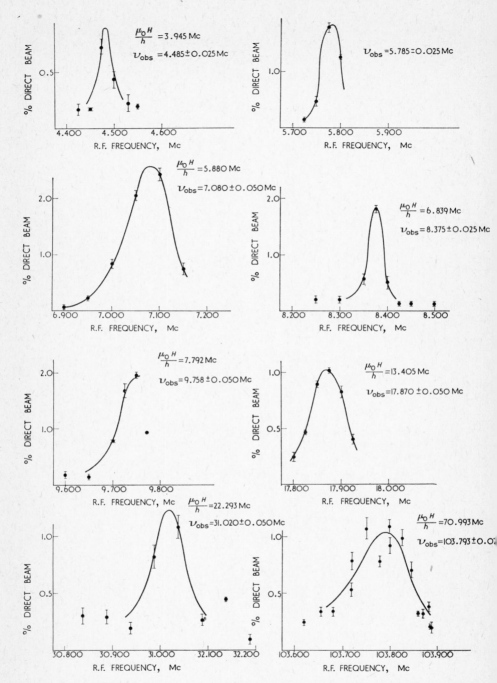

Fig. 25. The $J = 1$, $F = \frac{3}{2}$, double quantum transition followed as a function of the field to about 100 Mc/sec.

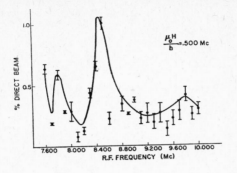

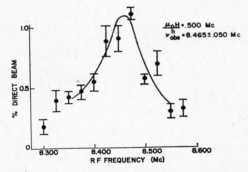

Fig. 26. $\Delta F = 1$ transition, the "direct" hyperfine transition.

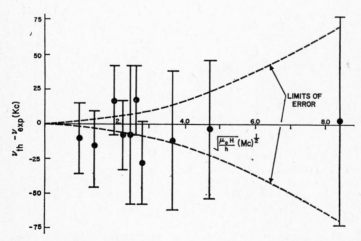

Fig. 27 The difference between observed resonances and those predicted based on the values of the constants assigned in the text.

there is little choice. The multielectron problem is very complicated, but fortunately a closed formula (non-relativistic) can be given for the hyperfine structure constant of a Hund's rule ground state atom that involves only one incomplete shell. The formula is useful in that the only atomic constant that need be evaluated is $\langle l|1/r^3|l\rangle$ for a single valence electron. If the hyperfine structure interaction is $a\mathbf{I} \cdot \mathbf{J}$, the expression is

$$a(J) = 2g_I\mu_0^2\langle l|r^{-3}|l\rangle \left[\frac{J(J+1)+L(L+1)-S(S+1)}{2J(J+1)} + \right.$$

$$+ \frac{2(2L-n^2)}{n^2(2L-1)(2l-1)(2l+3)}\left\{\frac{L(L+1)[J(J+1)+S(S+1)-L(L+1)]}{2J(J+1)} - \right.$$

$$\left.\left.- \frac{3[J(J+1)-L(L+1)-S(S+1)][J(J+1)+L(L+1)-S(S+1)]}{4J(J+1)}\right\}\right], \quad (16)$$

where n is the number of electrons if the shell is half filled or less, or n is the number of holes if the shell is half-filled or more. If there are two incomplete shells and each obey Hund's rule, the above result applies to each, and they can be easily combined. Eq. (16) applied to the ^7F multiplet of the $(5f)^6$ electrons yields

$$a(J) = g_I\mu_0^2\langle r^{-3}\rangle_{5f}\left[\frac{J(J+1)+58}{90}\right], \quad (17)$$

and

$$a(1) = \tfrac{2}{3}g_I\mu_0^2\langle r^{-3}\rangle_{5f}. \quad (18)$$

Using the best available wave functions, the value obtained for $\langle r^{-3}\rangle$ is $3.9a_0^{-3}$ and a is found to be $120\,g_I$ Mc/sec, from which the magnetic moment of Pu is calculated to be ± 0.02 nuclear magnetons.

While it is of no immediate application, an equally useful formula for Hund's rule ground states of incomplete single shells can be easily written down for the quadrupole interaction. It is

$$b = \frac{2L(2l-2n+1)}{(L+S)(2L+2S-1)(2l-1)(2l+3)}J(2J-1)e^2Q\langle l|1/r^3|l\rangle. \quad (19)$$

This is the b of Eq. (4). Q is the nuclear quadrupole moment according to the usual definition. If the shell is half full or less, n is the number of electrons and $b \geqq 0$. If the shell is half full or more, n is the number of holes and $b \leqq 0$.

TABLE 5

ISOTOPES INVESTIGATED BY ATOMIC BEAM TECHNIQUES AT THE UNIVERSITY OF CALIFORNIA

(Complete to October 16, 1957)

Isotope	Half-life	Spin	Magnetic moment (n.m.)	$Q(\times 10^{24})cm^2$	Hyperfine structure (Mc/sec)
$_{29}Cu^{61}$	3.3 h	3/2			
$_{31}Ga^{66}$	9.4 h	0	$\leq 10^{-3}$		
Ga^{67}	78 h	3/2	$+1.84(2)$	$+.213(12)$	$W_{32} = 597.2(26)$
					$W_{21} = 278.8(40)$
$_{37}Rb^{81}$	4.7 h	3/2	$+2.05(2)$		$5097(13)$
Rb^{81m}	31.5 m	9/2			
Rb^{82}	6.3 h	5	$+1.50(2)$		$3094.1(24)$
Rb^{83}	83 d	5/2	$+1.42(2)$		$3183.3(58)$
Rb^{84}	33 d	2	$-1.32(2)$		$3077.5(51)$
$_{47}Ag^{105}$	40 d	1/2			
Ag^{106}	8.6 d	6			
Ag^{110m}	253 d	6			
$_{53}I^{123}$	13 h	5/2			
$_{55}Cs^{127}$	6.2 h	1/2	$+1.44(13)$		$8960(200)$
Cs^{129}	31 h	1/2	$+1.48(3)$		$9230(200)$
Cs^{130}	30 m	1	$+1.37(8)$ (or $-1.45(8)$)		$6420(350)$ or $6800(350)$
Cs^{132}	6.2 d	2	$+2.22(2)$		$8653(30)$
$_{79}Au^{194}$	39 h	1			
$_{81}Tl^{197}$	2.8 h	1/2			
Tl^{198m}	1.9 h	7			
Tl^{199}	7.4 h	1/2			
Tl^{204}	4 y	2	$\pm.0894(20)$		$732(5)$
$_{94}Pu^{239}$	24,000 y	1/2	(for $J=1$, $g_J = -1.4975(10)$ and $W_{\frac{3}{2},\frac{1}{2}}=7.715(60)$)		

B. UNPUBLISHED DATA*

Isotope	Half-life	Spin
$_{19}K^{43}$	22 h	3/2
$_{31}Ga^{68}$	68 m	1
Br^{82}	36 h	5
$_{53}I^{124}$	4.5 d	2
$_{79}Au^{191}$	3 h	3/2
Au^{192}	4.8 h	1
Au^{193}	17 h	3/2
Au^{195}	185 d	3/2
Au^{196}	5.6 d	2
$_{83}Bi^{206}$	6.4 d	6
$_{95}Am^{241}$	461 yr	5/2

* Most of these results have been submitted for publication.

D

C. Measurements which have been made Elsewhere First but Reverified at Berkeley

Isotope	Half-life	Spin
$_{55}Cs^{131}$	10 d	5/2
$_{19}K^{42}$	12.5 h	2
$_{53}I^{131}$	8 d	7/2

REFERENCES

[1] George Bemski, "Fluorine Resonance in Molecular Beams," Thesis, University of California, Berkeley, 1953; Bemski, Nierenberg, and Silsbee, *Phys. Rev.* **98**, 470 (1955).

[2] Hobson, Hubbs, Nierenberg, and Silsbee, *Phys. Rev.* **96**, 1450 (1954).

[3] Hobson, Hubbs, Nierenberg, Silsbee, and Sunderland, *Phys. Rev.* **104**, 101 (1956).

[4] Nierenberg, Shugart, Silsbee and Sunderland, *Phys. Rev.* **104**, 1380 (1956).

[5] Hubbs, Nierenberg, Shugart, and Worcester, *Phys. Rev.* **105**, 1928 (1957); Worcester, Hubbs, and Nierenberg, *Bull. Am. Phys. Soc.* II, **2**, 316 (1957).

[6] Brink, Hubbs, Nierenberg, and Worcester, *Phys. Rev.* **107**, 189 (1957); Brink, Hubbs, Nierenberg, and Worcester, *Bull. Am. Phys. Soc.* II, **2**, 200 (1957).

[7] Hubbs, Marrus, Nierenberg, and Worcester, *Bull. Am. Phys. Soc.* II, **2**, 316 (1957).

[8] W. A. Nierenberg, The Static Moments of Radioactive Nuclei, *Annual Reviews of Nuclear Science* **7** (1957); John G. King and Jerrold R. Zacharias, Some New Applications and Techniques of Molecular Beams, *Advances in Electronics and Electron Physics*, Vol. VIII, 1956, Academic Press, Inc., New York.

[9] See reference 8. The first use of this technique was by J. R. Zacharias, *Phys. Rev.* **61**, 270 (1942).

[10] Reynolds, Christensen, Hooke, Hamilton, Stroke, Ewbank, Nierenberg, Shugart, and Silsbee, *Bull. Am. Phys. Soc.* II, **2**, 317 (1957); Ewbank, Marino, Shugart, and Silsbee *Bull. Am. Phys. Soc.* II, **3**, 185 (1958).

[11] E. H. Bellamy and K. F. Smith, *Phil. Mag.* **44**, 33 (1953).

[12] The work on the Ga isotopes was conducted principally by J. C. Hubbs, R. Marrus, and J. L. Worcester, and the work on the halogens by E. Lipworth, H. L. Garvin, and T. M. Green [e.g. *Bull. Am. Phys. Soc.* II, **2**, 316 (1957); II, **2**, 344 (1957)]. Some of this work has been published and some has been submitted for publication.

[13] Reference 5 and particularly the thesis of J. L. Worcester, University of California, Berkeley, 1956.

[14] E. Lipworth and H. L. Garvin, *Bull. Am. Phys. Soc.* II, **2**, 316 (1957); Thomas M. Green, Hugh L. Garvin, Edgar Lipworth, and W.A. Nierenberg, *Bull. Am. Phys. Soc.* II, **2**, 383 (1957); E. Lipworth, H. L. Garvin, and T. M. Green, *Bull. Am. Phys. Soc.* II, **2**, 344 (1957); Hugh L. Garvin, Thomas M. Green, and Edgar Lipworth, *Bull. Am. Phys. Soc.* II, **2**, 344 (1957).

[15] W. A. Nierenberg, A Method for Minimizing a Function of n Variables, UCRL-3816 (1957).

[16] Hubbs, Marrus, Nierenberg, and Worcester, *Bull. Am. Phys. Soc.* II, **2**, 316 (1957); Hubbs, Marrus, Nierenberg, and Worcester, *Phys. Rev.* **109**, 390 (1958).

3

Velocity Distributions in
Potassium Molecular Beams*

P. M. MARCUS and J. H. McFEE

Carnegie Institute of Technology
Pittsburgh, Pennsylvania

I. Introduction

This paper describes velocity distribution measurements made on potassium molecular beams with a fixed-frequency, variable phase velocity selector. The measurements are believed to be of high accuracy, and were taken over a wide range of oven pressures (0.84×10^{-3} mm Hg to 0.58 mm Hg).

The work described here is a continuation of work by A. Bennett and I. Estermann. The molecular beam apparatus was designed and constructed by Bennett[1] who also used the equipment to measure the velocity distribution in potassium beams. Comparison of his results with the Maxwell-Boltzmann distribution showed the marked effects of oven-slit geometry on the velocity distributions, and indicated a substantial deficiency of low-velocity molecules at moderately high oven pressures.[1] In all these measurements there was an uncertainty in the transit time of molecules passing through the selector of about 3% of the most probable transit time. If the measured and calculated most probable transit-times agreed to within this uncertainty, a factor was applied which made the position of the peaks coincide. Since Bennett's work, a number of refinements (which are described below) have been made which permit more accurate velocity measurements. In particular, a more accurate method of transit-time measurement has been devised, and no adjustment is now made in the position of the maximum of the measured velocity distribution when comparing it to the theoretical distribution. The uncertainty in the transit time is now less than 1% of the most probable transit time. Comparison of the present measurements with theoretical curves derived from the

* Work supported by the Office of Naval Research.

43

Maxwell distribution indicates a considerable deficiency of low-velocity molecules at the highest oven pressures. At the lowest oven pressures there is good agreement between the measured and theoretical curves.

Measurements of the velocity distribution in a potassium beam after reflection from a solid surface are now being attempted. Comparison of these with the direct-beam measurements should yield detailed information about the energy exchange between the beam and the surface.

II. Description of Apparatus

(a) General

Figure 1 is a plan view of the beam apparatus. An expanded scale is used for the slits to show their relative size. The "collimating" slit

TOP VIEW OF BEAM APPARATUS

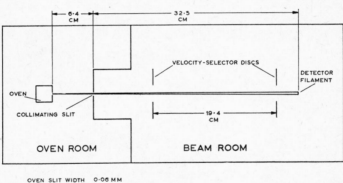

OVEN SLIT WIDTH   0·06 MM
COLLIMATING SLIT WIDTH 0·40 MM
DETECTOR FILAMENT WIDTH 0·34 MM

Fig. 1. Top view of beam apparatus showing dimensions. Expanded scale was used for slits and detector filament.

is narrow enough to provide sufficient isolation of the beam room from the oven room, but it does not define the beam. The beam is defined by the oven slit and the detector filament so that the effective path of the beam can be changed by moving the detector filament. The oven, velocity selector and detector are mounted on an optical bench and aligned optically, then inserted in a cylindrical vacuum chamber. The circular plate on the left divides the chamber into the separate oven, room and beam room.

(b) Oven

The oven shown in Fig. 2 is made entirely from copper to minimize thermal gradients. The potassium, sealed in a glass capsule, is placed in a hole in the plug. The front end of the capsule is broken off by pressure when the plug is tightened. The plug is chrome-plated to prevent jamming of copper threads. Clogging of the slits due to creep of potassium is minimized by holding the capsule in a vertical position.

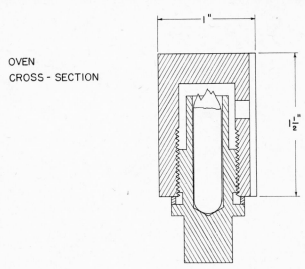

OVEN
CROSS - SECTION

Fig. 2. Oven cross-section (side view) showing threaded plug holding capsule of potassium.

(c) Oven Slit

In all the measurements described in this paper, thin foil (0.001 in. stainless steel) slit edges were used. The oven slit construction is practically identical with the "ideal" slit used by Miller and Kusch.[2]

(d) Detector

A surface-ionization detector was used, consisting of a strip 2 cm long × 0.3 mm wide × 0.002 in. thick, rolled out from suitable Pt, Mo, or W wire. Pt and Mo were found to be most satisfactory for measuring weak beams since the positive-ion background current emitted by these metals is very small in comparison to W. (Various W specimens were tried, including some "undoped" specimens by courtesy of Mr. J. S. Petro of the General Electric Company Lamp Wire and Phosphors Dept.)

A direct test for possible velocity sensitivity of the detecting filament was made by taking two successive velocity spectra differing only by substitution of a Pt for a W filament (by internal exchange of the filaments). The spectra showed identical relative intensity distributions, although the Pt detection efficiency was only about 80% of the W detection efficiency.

An Applied Physics Corp. Mod. 31 vibrating-reed electrometer was used to measure the ion current produced by the detector.

(e) Velocity-selector

The velocity selector consists of two identical slotted discs (Fig. 3). Each disc is turned by an 8000 rpm synchronous motor. A phase-shifter* varies the phase of the voltage fed to one motor relative to the

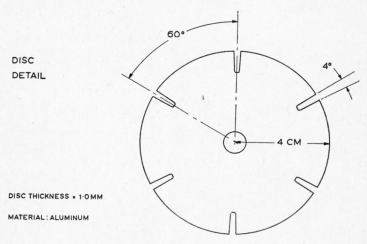

Fig. 3. Detail of selector disc.

other. As is described below, a light beam is used to determine when the velocity selector is set for zero transit-time. This beam is produced by a small light source near one disc. It then passes through the velocity selector underneath the motors, and is detected by a photo-cell near the other disc. The motors use miniature precision ball bearings which are lubricated when installed with a small drop of diffusion pump oil. A pressure of $\leqslant 5 \times 10^{-7}$ mm Hg can be maintained indefinitely in the beam room with the motors running.

* A differential generator (i.e. a type of transformer in which one winding can be rotated with respect to the other) is used as a phase-shifter.

III. Action of the Velocity-Selector

As explained in Appendix I, if the setting of the phase-shifter is such that the delay time of the second disc relative to the first is τ, and the slit open time is β, then the number of beam particles passing through the selector (per cm^2 of beam cross-section) each time a pair of slits— one slit in one disc, one slit in the other disc—cuts the beam (call this one pass) will be given by

$$h(\tau, \beta) = \int\limits_0^\infty S(\tau, T, \beta) I(T) dT. \tag{1}$$

T is the transit time (between discs of separation l), $I(T)dT$ is the incident intensity in the range dT (molecules/cm^2 sec) and $S(\tau, T, \beta)$ is the "shutter function" (secs) describing the transmission of the velocity selector for a given phase setting (it is the effective open time in a single pass for molecules of transit time T).

If the effusion from the oven is ideal, $I(T)$ will simply be the "Maxwell beam intensity function" (ref. 4, p. 20), in the transit-time variable. It is convenient to use dimensionless variables obtained by dividing by T_0, the transit-time of the most probable velocity in the oven. Defining the reduced transit-time

$$\bar{T} = \frac{T}{T_0} \text{ where } T_0 = l \Big/ \sqrt{\frac{2R T_K}{M}}; \ T_K = \text{absolute temperature} \tag{2}$$

we have

$$I(T) dT = \frac{2I_0}{\bar{T}^5} e^{-(1/\bar{T})^2}.d\bar{T}, \tag{3}$$

which has a form independent of temperature. I_0 is the total beam intensity (molecules/cm^2 sec). $I(T)$ is plotted as the solid curve in Fig. 4.

The shutter function $S(\tau, T, \beta)$ is an isosceles triangle as a function of T, base 2β, peak β (at $T = \tau$), if beam width and disc thickness are negligible. The reduced shutter function S/T_0 is shown in Fig. 4, (for typical values of $\beta = 0.850 \times 10^{-4}$ sec and $T_0 = 4.557 \times 10^{-4}$ sec). Since T_0 depends on temperature, S/T_0 does also. The integral of the product of $I(\bar{T}) d\bar{T}$ and S/T_0 is proportional to $h(\tau, \beta)$ and is plotted in Fig. 4 (dotted curve) as a function of reduced delay time τ/T_0.

Both I and h in Fig. 4 are normalized to the same arbitrary peak value to show the effect of the velocity selector on the breadth and shape of the curves. On the reduced transit-time scale h, but not I, is slightly temperature dependent.

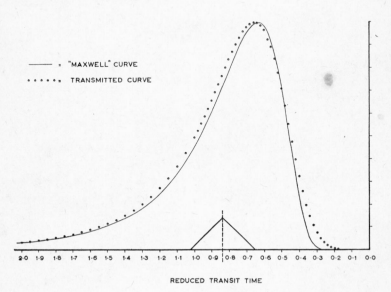

Fig. 4. Maxwell incident beam intensity curve vs. reduced transit-time and theoretical transmitted curve vs. reduced delay time showing effect of transmission through velocity selector. Triangle is ideal shutter function for reduced delay time = 0.84.

Appropriate dimensionless forms for I and h which make them directly comparable are given in Appendix I and plotted in Fig. 9.

In calculating theoretical transmission curves to compare with the measured curves, the following effects were considered which could give rise to differences from the dotted curve shown in Fig. 4.

1. The finite angular spread of the beam may be shown to have a negligible effect on the transmitted curve.*

2. The finite disc thickness causes a small but not negligible distortion of the transmitted curve. At twice the most probable transit-time the curve is reduced by 2% relative to the peak.* (This correction was not explicitly introduced in the calculated curves of Figs. 5 and 6.)

* See Appendix II.

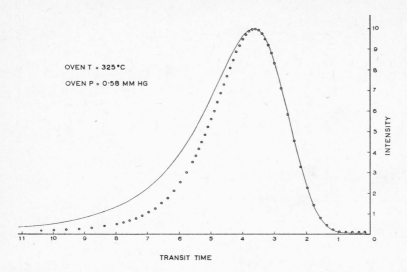

Fig. 5. Measured transmission curve (circles) and calculated Maxwell transmission curve (solid line) at high oven temperature (325° C) and beam intensity. Abscissa is delay time τ, which is approximately transit time of molecules transmitted (1 unit of $\tau = 0.708 \times 10^{-4}$ sec $= 3\frac{1}{3}°$ phase shift). Ordinates are in arbitrary units; curves normalized to same maximum value.

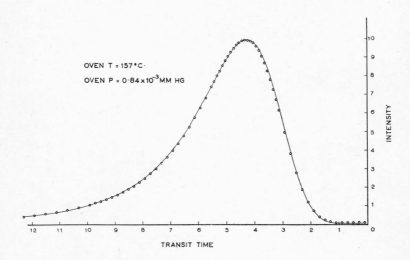

Fig. 6. Measured transmission curve and calculated Maxwell transmission curve at low oven temperature (157° C) and beam intensity. Details as for Fig. 5.

3. The second-order velocity spectrum due to slow molecules with T greater than the time interval between slots gives a small contribution which is a maximum ($\frac{1}{2}\%$ of peak) at zero on the transit-time scale. This correction is taken into account in the calculated curves of Figs. 5 and 6. Third-order and all higher-order spectra taken together have been shown to be negligible.*

IV. Alignment of the Apparatus

The critical measurement for this type of velocity-selector is that of the relative phase angle between the two discs. In order to compare an experimental curve to a calculated curve, one must know not only how much this phase angle changes for a given change in the phase-shifter setting, but also what phase-shifter setting corresponds to zero phase, i.e. to zero transit-time.

That the relative phase angle of the discs is proportional to the setting of the phase-shifter to within 0.1° has been determined by direct visual observation.[3] This was accomplished by inscribing a degree scale on one disc, and a vernier scale on the other. A disc-shaped mirror was placed half-way between the two discs so that the image of the vernier appeared superimposed on the degree scale. The direct observation of phase shift was then made by a stroboscopic flash.

The determination of zero transit-time setting for the molecular beam is accomplished with the aid of a light beam. The photons have effectively zero transit-time compared to molecule transit-times. Thus $I(T)$ for the photons is a delta function at $T = 0$, and the transmitted curve for the light beam is simply the triangular shutter function shown in Fig. 4 (provided the angular spread of the light beam is small). The peak of this triangle indicates zero transit-time, but this will be zero transit-time for the molecular beam only if the light beam and molecular beam are parallel in a "rolled-out" view of the velocity selector— (lack of parallelism shifts the velocity distribution with respect to the light beam peak). The condition of parallelism can be obtained as follows:

(a) The difference between the phase-shifter setting corresponding to the peak of the light-beam triangle and the setting corresponding to a definite transit-time on the molecular beam distribution curve is measured (the half-maximum point on the steep side of the curve is usually chosen).

(b) The direction of rotation of the discs is reversed, and the measurement described in (a) is repeated. (Reversal of rotation of the discs

* See Appendix II.

reverses the shift of the velocity distribution with respect to the light beam.)

(c) The molecular beam is adjusted (by moving the detector filament horizontally and in a direction perpendicular to the beam) to make the above two measurements equal. This can be done to within 0.1°, i.e. to within about 1/30 of a unit on the transit time scale of Fig. 5 and 6.

In practice the relative phase angle is never constant in time but fluctuates due to changing torques applied by the motor bearings. In order to keep these fluctuations well below 0.1°, the bearings must be replaced periodically and the motor driving-voltage must be kept sufficiently high. Even with these precautions, a "run-in" time of 15 min. to 1 hour is found to be necessary each time the motors are turned on. During the "run-in" period the relative phase will at first vary quite wildly ($\sim 1°$ or so). The fluctuations then gradually die down to $\sim 0.02°$ if the bearings are in good condition. This much phase shift is easily observable by using either the light beam or the molecular beam.

V. Experimental Results

Figures 5 and 6 are comparisons between experimental results and transmitted curves calculated on the basis of ideal effusion (Maxwell transmission curves). The curves are all normalized to the same maximum value. However, the transit-time scale is fixed by using the measured zero of transit-time and the curves are not adjusted by horizontal translation. The data were taken in a point-by-point fashion in order to eliminate distortion of the distribution curve due to response time of the detector. The zero-line and maximum of the curve were checked frequently during the recording of each distribution in order to minimize the effects of zero-line drift and changes in the beam intensity. In both Fig. 5 and Fig. 6, 18 divisions on the transit-time scale corresponds to a phase shift equal to the angular spacing between the slits in the velocity-selector discs (60° in present case). Therefore, zero on the transit-time scale is also 18 (the second-order spectrum), 36 (the third-order spectrum), etc.

Figure 5 shows an experimental curve for a high oven pressure. The mean free path in the oven is about equal to the slit width. The following features are of interest:

1. The agreement with the calculated curve is very good on the high-velocity side of the maximum, but there is a marked deficiency of low-velocity atoms amounting to about 60% of the calculated value at twice the most probable transit-time.

2. At zero transit-time the experimental curve has roughly twice the amplitude of the calculated curve.

In Fig. 6 the mean free path in the oven is hundreds of times greater than the slit width. Here the important features are:

1. The general agreement on the low-velocity side of the curves is now very good. The deficiency is about 2% of the calculated value at twice the most probable transit-time.

2. The measured intensities at the zero phase position are again in excess of the calculated intensities; the intensities are small (1% of the peak) but measurable. In fact, the experimental curve is higher than the calculated curve from about $9\frac{1}{2}$ onward on the transit-time axis. (After moving the shutter position to reduce its effect on the background signal and decreasing the disc thickness at the slit edge, this excess measured intensity was not observed in later measurements.)

3. Agreement on the high-velocity side is not as good as at the higher oven pressure. There is a 2% deficiency at the half-maximum point.

4. The peak of the measured curve is shifted toward longer transit-times by about 1.5% of the corresponding transit time as compared to the calculated curve.

Effects 3 and 4 can almost be accounted for by the quoted uncertainty in the transit-time measurement. More data are needed to determine if these discrepancies are real.

Figure 7 summarizes the results of ten velocity distribution measurements, each taken at a different oven temperature. All the points refer to a transit time equal to twice the most probable transit time. The scatter on this plot, about 3% (1% of the maximum amplitude), gives some idea of the reproducibility of the data. As noted above there appears to be a residual 2% deficiency present at the lowest oven pressures. Most of this would be removed if the calculated curves had taken into account the thickness of the velocity-selector discs (see Appendix II). However, this also increases the excess which is observed at longer transit-times. (As explained above, this excess was probably spurious. Later measurements made with the shutter positioned at the center of the beam room, rather than directly on the oven side of the collimating slit, have not shown any excess.)

Also plotted on Fig. 7 are two points taken from the potassium data of Miller and Kusch.[2] Bennett's results for knife-edge oven slits indicate low-velocity deficiencies which are several times greater than those reported here. A comparison was also made with the earlier gravity free-fall experiment of Estermann, Simpson, and Stern[5] who used cesium beams. Their results showed low-velocity deficiencies considerably larger than those reported here for potassium.

The observed deficiency is thus an effect of high beam intensity, and may arise partly from self scattering in the beam, as roughly calculated by Estermann, Simpson, and Stern,[5] and partly from deviations from ideal effusion conditions at the oven slit, when the mean free path is

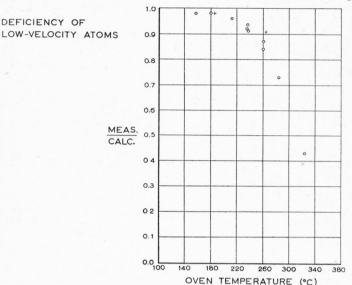

Fig. 7. Fraction of transmitted Maxwell intensity observed at twice the most probable transit-time as a function of oven temperature. $(1 - (\text{meas./calc.}) = $ deficiency.) Circles are the data of this report. Crosses are taken from the data of Miller and Kusch,[2] Runs No. 57 and 60.

short. The velocity dependence of residual gas scattering at a pressure 5×10^{-7} mm Hg does not appear to be significant, as shown by agreement of measured with calculated transmission curves at the lowest beam intensities, and by direct calculation assuming quite large scattering cross-sections (400 Å² for K against air molecules). This conclusion is in agreement with Miller and Kusch,[2] p. 1320.

The measured and calculated Maxwell transmission curves (corrected for higher-order spectra) for low-pressure beams agree fairly well in all respects, although small residual discrepancies as noted above, still persist. The reproducibility and precision should be adequate to detect the small changes in velocity spectra produced by reflection at solid surfaces.

REFERENCES

1. A. I. Bennett and I. Estermann, "Distribution of Velocities in Molecular Beams of Potassium", (Doctoral Dissertation, Carnegie Institute of Technology, 1953).
2. R. C. Miller and P. Kusch, Velocity Distributions in Potassium and Thallium Atomic Beams, *Phys. Rev.* **99**, 1314 (1955).
3. A. I. Bennett, The Phase-Shift Velocity Selector (to be published).
4. N. F. Ramsey, "Molecular Beams", Oxford 1956.
5. I. Estermann, O. C. Simpson, and O. Stern, The Free Fall of Atoms and the Measurement of the Velocity Distribution in a Molecular Beam of Cesium Atoms, *Phys. Rev.* **71**, 238 (1947).

Acknowledgement

The authors would like to thank Dr. I. Estermann of the U.S. Office of Naval Research for his interest and encouragement during the course of this work, Dr. A. I. Bennett of the Westinghouse Research Laboratories for generously contributing time and technical advice during all aspects of this research, and Dr. S. A. Friedberg of Carnegie Institute of Technology for many helpful discussions and suggestions.

APPENDIX I

TRANSMISSION FORMULAS FOR THE PHASE-SHIFT VELOCITY SELECTOR

1. *Definitions and magnitudes of physical quantities*

The following quantities occur in the discussion of the behavior of the velocity selector, and are given here for convenient reference, together with typical magnitudes for the instruments in use.

β = slit open time = 0.850×10^{-4} sec (corresponding to an angular aperture of 4.03°, and rotation speed of the discs of 132 rev/sec).

l = spacing between discs (front surface to front surface) = 19.5 cm.

α = most probable velocity in the oven

$$= \sqrt{\frac{2RT_K}{M}} = 4.611 \times 10^4 \left(\frac{T_K}{500}\right)^{\frac{1}{2}} \frac{\text{cm}}{\text{sec}}$$

for potassium (T_K = Kelvin temperature).

T = l/v = transit time for molecules of velocity v.

T_0 = l/α = transit time of most probable velocity

$$= 4.229 \times 10^{-4} \left(\frac{500}{T_K}\right)^{\frac{1}{2}} \text{ sec.}$$

$I(T)dT$ = incident intensity at first disc in range dT (molecules/cm² sec).

$$I_0 = \int_0^\infty I(T)\,dT =$$

= total intensity at first disc (molecules/cm^2 sec).

τ = time delay of slit in second disc with respect to slit in first disc.

t = time, $t = 0$ when leading edge of slit in first disc first reaches the beam line (the angular spread of the beam is taken as infinitesimal; see Appendix II, 1, for discussions of this approximation).

$h(\tau, \beta)$ = the transmission function, the number of molecules per cm^2 of beam cross section transmitted during one pass of a pair of slits, for given time delay τ.

Reduced or dimensionless quantities are indicated by a bar.

$\bar{T} = T/T_0$, $\bar{\tau} = \tau/T_0$, $\bar{\beta} = \beta/T_0$ are the reduced transit time, reduced delay time, and reduced slit open time (dimensionless).

Reduced transmission functions $\bar{h}$, and beam intensity functions $\bar{I}$ will be defined later.

2. *Derivation and properties of the transmission function*

The measured intensity is $h(\tau, \beta)$, (times the frequency at which a slit passes the beam line, 800/sec), which must therefore be related to the intensity distribution in the incident beam $I(T)$. A simple description of this relationship follows from consideration of the pairs of values of T and t', the arrival time at the first disc, which give a transmitted molecule. Figure 8 shows the quadrangular area on a T, t' plane which gives transmission. The first slit is open from $t = 0$ to β,* hence all molecules with arrival times $0 \leqslant t' \leqslant \beta$ pass through it. For each t', there is a range of T for which the molecules reach the second slit during its open time τ to $\tau + \beta$, namely from $T = \tau - t'$ to $T = \tau + \beta - t'$.

$I(T)\,dT\,dt'$ is the number of molecules/cm^2 arriving at the first disc in range dT during time interval dt', hence

$$h(\tau, \beta) = \int_0^\beta dt' \int_{\tau-t'}^{\tau+\beta-t'} dT\, I(T) = \int_{\tau-\beta}^\tau dT \int_{\tau-T}^\beta dt'\, I(T) + \int_\tau^{\tau+\beta} dT \int_0^{\tau+\beta-T} dt'\, I(T)\dagger \qquad (A.1)$$

* Note it is again open from 15β to 16β, 30β to 31β, etc.

† The actual transmitted intensity at the detector is reduced from $h(\tau, \beta)$ in (A.1) by the square of the source to first disc distance divided by the square of the source to detector distance.

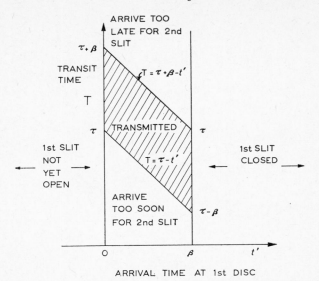

Fig. 8. Transmission diagram of velocity selector. Shaded area shows pairs of transit-times and arrival-times resulting in transmission.

From the second form of (A.1), integrating over t' gives;

$$h(\tau, \beta) = \int_0^\infty S(\tau, \beta, T) I(T) dT \qquad (A.2)$$

where the shutter function $S(\tau, \beta, T)$ is

$$S(\tau, \beta, T) = \begin{cases} T+\beta-\tau \text{ for } \tau-\beta \leqslant T \leqslant \tau \\ \tau+\beta-T \text{ for } \tau \leqslant T \leqslant \tau+\beta. \\ \quad 0 \qquad \text{otherwise} \end{cases} \qquad (A.3)$$

Note that

$$I(T) = 0 \text{ for } T < 0, \qquad (A.4)$$

hence integration in (A.1) and (A.2) for $T < 0$ makes no contribution to $h(\tau, \beta)$.

Differentiating (A.1) twice with respect to τ gives the relationship of h to I, namely

$$\frac{\partial^2 h(\tau, \beta)}{\partial \tau^2} = I(\tau+\beta) - 2I(\tau) + I(\tau-\beta), \qquad (A.5)$$

thus the second derivative of h equals the second finite difference of I at interval β; in compact form,

$$h''(\tau, \beta) = \Delta^2_\beta I(\tau).$$

One relation satisfied by h is noteworthy: if the pulse of molecules passing the first slit is broken into transit-time ranges by a series of values of τ separated by β, the ranges are contiguous and account for all molecules in the pulse, hence

$$\sum_{n=0,1,2}^{\infty} h(\tau_0 + n\beta, \beta) = \beta \int_0^\infty I(T)\,dT = \beta I_0 \; ; \tau_0 < 0. \qquad \text{(A.6)}$$

The evaluation of $I(T)$ requires solution of the difference equation (A.5) given $h(\tau, \beta)$, hence all derivatives of h, from the measured intensities. Several procedures have been suggested by Bennett.[1,3] We note one useful result. If $\Delta_\beta^2 I(\tau)$ in (A.5) is expanded in derivatives of $I(\tau)$ at τ, only even orders occur, and

$$h''(\tau, \beta) = \beta^2\, I''(\tau) + \frac{\beta^4}{12}\, I^{IV}(\tau) + \dots \qquad \text{(A.7)}$$

Integration of (A.7) and further differentiation of (A.7) permit its inversion in the form

$$I(\tau) = \frac{h(\tau, \beta)}{\beta^2} - \frac{1}{12} h''(\tau, \beta) + \frac{\beta^2}{240} h^{IV}(\tau, \beta) - \dots \qquad \text{(A.8)}$$

Evaluation of h and its derivatives from the measurement then permits $I(\tau)$ to be calculated from (A.8).

For calculation purposes it is convenient to define dimensionless beam intensity and transmission functions. Thus I/I_0 = fraction of molecules in the beam per unit transit-time. Hence

$$\bar{I}(\bar{T}) = \frac{T_0 I(T)}{I_0} = \qquad \text{(A.9)}$$

= the fraction of molecules per unit reduced transit-time, is a dimensionless beam intensity function. It satisfies the condition

$$\int_0^\infty \bar{I}(\bar{T})\,d\bar{T} = 1 \; ; \qquad \text{(A.10)}$$

where $\bar{T} = T/T_0$ is the reduced transit-time variable.

E

Similarly $[h(\tau, \beta)/I_0\beta]$ = fraction of the molecules admitted by the first slit which are in the transmitted pulse for time delay τ and open time β of the slits. Hence

$$\bar{h}(\bar{\tau}, \bar{\beta}) = \frac{h(\tau, \beta)}{I_0\beta \, \beta/T_0} = \tag{A.11}$$

= fraction of admitted molecules in transmitted pulse per unit reduced open time, is a dimensionless transmission function comparable to $\bar{I}(\bar{T})$. Thus

$$\sum_{n=0,1,2,\ldots}^{\infty} \bar{h}(\bar{\tau}_0 + n\bar{\beta}, \bar{\beta})\left(\frac{\beta}{T_0}\right) = 1$$

by (A.6). Then approximating the sum by an integral, we have

$$\int_{-\bar{\beta}}^{\infty} \bar{h}(\bar{\tau}, \bar{\beta}) \, d\bar{\tau} \cong 1 \tag{A.12}$$

where $\bar{\tau} = \tau/T_0$ is the reduced delay time, and for $\bar{\tau} < -\bar{\beta}$, the lower limit, the integrand vanishes. (A.12) is the analogue of (A.10), and shows that the two dimensionless functions $\bar{I}(\bar{\tau})$ and $\bar{h}(\bar{\tau}, \bar{\beta})$ integrated with respect to $\bar{\tau}$ each have unit area, hence are appropriate for comparison to show the transmission effect of the velocity selector on the incident beam.

For the Maxwell intensity distribution (i.e. the intensity distribution in the beam for ideal effusion from an oven in equilibrium at one temperature)

$$\bar{I}(\bar{T}) = \frac{2}{\bar{T}^5} e^{-(1/\bar{T})^2}. \tag{A.13}$$

The corresponding distribution in velocity is

$$I(v)dv = 2I_0 \frac{v^3}{\alpha^3} e^{-v^2/\alpha^2} \frac{dv}{\alpha}$$

(see Ref. 4, p. 20.) The reduced transmission function for this incident intensity is

$$\bar{h}(\bar{\tau}, \bar{\beta}) = \frac{2}{\bar{\beta}^2} [K(\bar{\tau}+\bar{\beta}) - 2K(\bar{\tau}) + K(\bar{\tau}-\bar{\beta})]$$

$$\bar{\beta} = \beta/T_0, \quad K(x) = \frac{x}{2}e^{-(1/x)^2} + \frac{\sqrt{\pi}}{4}\left(\text{erf}\frac{1}{x} - 1\right) \tag{A.14}$$

$$\text{erf } t = \frac{2}{\sqrt{\pi}}\int_0^t e^{-t^2}dt.$$

A comparison of these functions is shown in Fig. 9, including the effect of the available range of temperature on $\bar{h}(\bar{\tau}, \bar{\beta})$. The velocity selector reduces the peak by about 6 to 9%, and broadens and shifts the distribution slightly with respect to the incident velocity distribution.

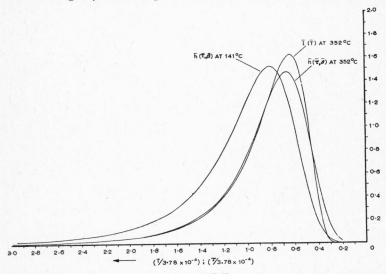

Fig. 9. Reduced Maxwell beam intensity $\bar{I}(\bar{T})$ and reduced transmission functions $\bar{h}(\bar{\tau}, \bar{\beta})$ at extremes of temperature (352° C and 141° C). The scale of τ, or T, is properly reduced at 352° C, where $T_0 = 3.78 \times 10^{-4}$ sec. At 141° C the $\bar{h}$ curve is then *not* plotted against the corresponding $\bar{\tau}$, but shows directly the effect of temperature on the transmission function in terms of the variable τ. (If it were plotted against that $\bar{\tau}$, the $\bar{h}$ for 141° C would lie very close to $\bar{h}$ for 352° C.)

APPENDIX II
CORRECTIONS TO THE IDEAL TRANSMISSION FUNCTION

The function $h(\tau, \beta)$ given by (A.1) is calculated under ideal conditions. Three types of corrections to (A.1) should be considered in interpreting the measurements made with the actual instrument, and these are now considered quantitatively.

1. Effects of Finite Angular Spread of the Beam

The finite angular width (in a plane tangential to the discs) introduces a range of delay times for each value of τ, the time delay of the second disc, since the beam line is now spread out in angle and different parts have different effective delay times. If l is the spacing between discs and φ is the beam angle (in radians), the range of delay times, $2w$, is

$$2w = \frac{l\varphi}{v} = \frac{l}{v}\frac{a}{L} \tag{A.15}$$

where v = velocity of the edge of the disc
  a = detector width
  L = oven to detector distance
as shown in Fig. 10.

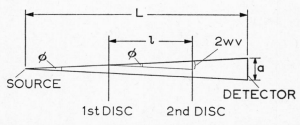

Fig. 10. Geometry of beam with angular spread φ. Diagram is in a plane which is tangent to the edges of the velocity selector discs.

The effect of this range of delay times is to superimpose a set of transmission functions from $\tau - w$ to $\tau + w$. Using (A.2) for $h(\tau, \beta)$ we can obtain the superposed average transmission function $h_w(\tau, \beta)$ by using an averaged shutter function, $S_w(\tau, \beta, T)$,

$$h_w(\tau, \beta) = \int_0^\infty S_w(\tau, \beta, T)\, I(T)\, dT \tag{A.16}$$

$$S_w(\tau, \beta, T) = \frac{1}{2w}\int_{\tau-w}^{\tau+w} S(\tau, \beta, T)\, d\tau = \frac{1}{2w}\int_{T-w}^{T+w} S(\tau, \beta, T)\, dT \tag{A.17}$$

where

$$S_w(\tau, \beta, T) = \begin{cases} 0 & , T \leqslant \tau - \beta - w \\ \dfrac{(T - \tau + \beta + w)^2}{4w} & , \tau - \beta - w \leqslant T \leqslant \tau - \beta + w \\ T - \tau + \beta & , \tau - \beta + w \leqslant T \leqslant \tau - w \end{cases} \tag{A.18}$$

$$S_w(\tau, \beta, T) = \begin{cases} \beta - \dfrac{w^2 + (\tau - T)^2}{2w} & , \tau - w \leqslant T \leqslant \tau + w \\ \tau + \beta - T & , \tau + w \leqslant T \leqslant \tau + \beta - w \\ \dfrac{(\tau - T + \beta + w)^2}{4w} & , \tau + \beta - w \leqslant T \leqslant \tau + \beta + w \\ 0 & , \tau + \beta + w \leqslant T \end{cases}$$

Equation (A.18) is the averaged shutter function symmetrical around $T = \tau$, with rounded corners shown in Fig. 11 for an exaggerated value of $\bar{w} = (w/T_0) = 0.025$ and $\bar{\beta} = 0.20$. This function has been used in a direct calculation of $h_w(\tau, \beta)$ from (A.16) for $I(T)$ a Maxwell distribution. The effect is smaller than our precision of measurement and at typical values for our apparatus ($\bar{w} = 0.005$, $\bar{\beta} = 0.20$) decreases the ratio of the intensity of slow molecules, say at twice the peak delay time relative to the peak, by about 0.02%. Larger values of w increase this ratio, as is shown in the following table.

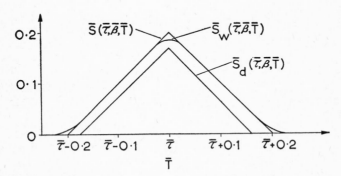

Fig. 11. Reduced shutter functions vs. reduced transit time.
$\bar{S} = (S/T_0)$ ideal shutter function.
$\bar{S}_w = (S_w/T_0)$ shutter function averaged over angular spread of beam.
$\bar{S}_d = (S_d/T_0)$ shutter function corrected for disc thickness.

TABLE 1

EFFECT OF FINITE ANGULAR SPREAD OF BEAM ON TRANSMISSION FUNCTION

(comparing value at $\bar{\tau} = 1.32$ with $\bar{\tau} = 0.66$, corresponding to the peak)

$\bar{w}$	$r_w = \dfrac{\bar{h}_w(1.32,\ 0.2083)}{\bar{h}_w(0.66,\ 0.2083)}$	% change $= \dfrac{(r_w - r_0)100}{r_0}$
0	0.19494	0
0.005	0.19491	−0.02
0.010	0.19506	+0.06
0.020	0.19531	+0.19
0.030	0.19581	+0.45
0.050	0.19740	+1.26
0.100	0.20499	+5.16
0.150	0.21536	+10.5

2. *Effects of Finite Disc Thickness*

The thickness d of the velocity selector discs decreases the effective open time of both entrance and exit slots for molecules of transit-time T from β to $\beta - (dT/l)$. Thus (l/T) is the velocity of a molecule of transit-time T, hence it must enter one side of the slot at least a time $d/(l/T)$ before the slot closes to clear the other side.

This effective open time evidently alters the ideal shutter function to

$$S_d(\tau, \beta, T) = \begin{cases} \beta - \tau + T\left(1 - \dfrac{d}{l}\right), & \dfrac{\tau - \beta}{1 - \dfrac{d}{l}} \leqslant T \leqslant \tau \\[4mm] \tau + \beta - T\left(1 + \dfrac{d}{l}\right), & \tau \leqslant T \leqslant \dfrac{\tau + \beta}{1 + \dfrac{d}{l}} \end{cases} \tag{A.19}$$

The thickness-corrected shutter function $S_d(\tau, \beta, T)$ is still a triangular function of T or τ, with straight sides, but with a lower peak and larger area toward longer transit-times.

Direct numerical integration using $S_d(\tau, \beta, T)$ and the Maxwell beam intensity function shows a reduction in transmission of several per cent at all delay times, least at the peak. The percentage decrease in transmission is shown in Table 2 at the typical value $d/l = 0.005$. The peak value $\bar{h}(\bar{\tau}_p, \bar{\beta})$ is lowered by 3%, where $\bar{\tau}_p =$ the reduced delay time of the peak ($\simeq 0.66$), whereas $\bar{h}(2\bar{\tau}_p, \bar{\beta})$ is lowered by 5%, thus creating a relative deficiency at long transit-times that must be considered in interpreting the measured transmission.

TABLE 2

EFFECT OF FINITE DISC THICKNESS ON TRANSMISSION FUNCTION

(at $\bar{\beta} = 0.2083$, and $d/l = 0.005$)

$\bar{\tau}$	$\bar{h}(\bar{\tau}, \bar{\beta})$	$\dfrac{100[\bar{h}(\bar{\tau}, \bar{\beta}) - \bar{h}_d(\bar{\tau}, \bar{\beta})]}{\bar{h}(\bar{\tau}, \bar{\beta})} = \%$ change
0.2	0.0125	6.4
0.4	0.5107	2.9
0.6	1.4339	2.7
0.8	1.2669	3.7
1.0	0.7561	4.8
1.5	0.1742	7.3
2.0	0.0497	9.7
2.5	0.0177	11.9

3. Effects of Higher-Order Spectra

The observed transmission function contains all the higher-order velocity spectra resulting from the long transit-time tail of the pulse passing through the first slot. If τ_0 = the delay time of the next slit after a given one (on the same disc), and $h_t(\tau, \beta)$ the total transmission function to all orders (but uncorrected for angular spread and thickness effects), then

$$h_t(\tau, \beta) = \sum_{n=0}^{\infty} h(\tau + n\tau_0, \beta) \qquad (A.20)$$

where $h(\tau, \beta)$ is the single pass transmission function. In the present design $\bar{\tau}_0$ is about $15\bar{\beta}$, and typical values of the successive spectra, at say, $\bar{\tau} = 0$, and $\bar{\beta} = 0.2083$ of the reduced transmission function $\bar{h}(\bar{\tau}, \bar{\beta})$ are

$$\bar{h}(0, \bar{\beta}) = 0 \; ; \bar{h}(15\bar{\beta}, \bar{\beta}) = 0.007 \; ; \bar{h}(30\bar{\beta}, \bar{\beta}) \simeq 0.0002 \text{ etc.} \qquad (A.21)$$

The sum of all terms after the second term in (A.21) (i.e. after the second-order spectrum) is less than 4% of that term which in turn is about 0.4% of the peak value. Hence the third and higher order spectra can be ignored.

4

Electron Magnetic Moment and Atomic Magnetism*

VERNON W. HUGHES

Yale University, New Haven, Connecticut

I. Introduction

The original stimulus for recent precise measurements of atomic electronic magnetic moments or g_J values was the interest in the spin magnetic moment of the electron. The discovery of the Lamb shift[1] and the disagreement of the measured value of the hyperfine structure splitting in hydrogen[2] with the value computed from the Fermi formula led to the suggestion that the spin magnetic moment of the electron is larger than 1 Bohr magneton.[3] Comparisons of experimentally determined g_J values in different atoms in states involving both orbital and spin electronic magnetic moments proved the existence of an anomalous magnetic moment of the electron about 0.1% larger than the Bohr magneton.[4]

The anomalous spin magnetic moment of the electron arises from virtual radiative processes involving photons and electron-positron pairs. On the basis of modern quantum electrodynamics its value has been computed to order α^2 (α = fine structure constant), and hence to an accuracy of about 1 part in a million.[5] The most accurate experimental determination is obtained from a comparison of the g_J value of hydrogen in its ground state with the orbital g value, g_l, of the free electron, and has an uncertainty of about 10 parts in a million.[6]

Atomic g_J values of many multielectron atoms have been measured to an accuracy of about 1 part in a million and the theory of atomic magnetism has been extended to order α^2 to include the relativistic as well as the virtual radiative contributions to atomic magnetism.[7] Particularly for the case of helium a strong confirmation of the theory of

* The preparation of this article was aided in part by the Office of Naval Research, the Air Force Office of Scientific Research and Development, and the National Science Foundation.

65

the relativistic contributions has been achieved.[8] Substantial discrepancies exist between the experimental and theoretical g_J values for many other multielectron atoms. The most likely explanation of these discrepancies appears to be the inadequacy of the atomic wavefunctions available for the computations, and hence experimentally determined g_J values can be used as a test for atomic wavefunctions. From another viewpoint, if adequate atomic Schroedinger wavefunctions were available for multielectron atoms, the highly precise experimental g_J values could be used to obtain the value of the spin magnetic moment of the electron to a higher precision than it is presently known from experiments on hydrogen and the free electron.

THEORY OF ATOMIC MAGNETISM

II. Electron spin magnetic moment

The Dirac theory of the electron predicts that the spin magnetic moment of the electron is 1 Bohr magneton

$$\left(\mu_0 = \frac{e\hbar}{2mc} \right)$$

and hence that the spin g-value of the electron is 2.

$$\left[g_s = \frac{\text{spin magnetic moment (in units of } \mu_0)}{\text{spin angular momentum (in units of } \hbar)} \right]$$

Corrections to the Dirac theory value of $g_s = 2$ arise due to virtual radiative processes. The order α and α^2 corrections have been computed by the modern covariant, renormalized theory of quantum electrodynamics[5] and the Feynman diagrams which contribute are shown in Fig. 1. The theoretical value is:

$$g_s = 2 \left[1 + \frac{\alpha}{2\pi} - 0.328 \frac{\alpha^2}{\pi^2} \right] \tag{1}$$

$$= 2 \left[1 + 0.0011614 - 0.0000018 \right] \tag{1a}$$

$$= 2 \left[1.0011596 \right] \tag{1b}$$

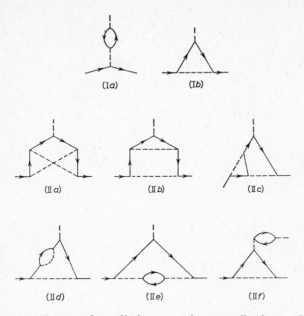

Fig. 1. Feynman diagrams for radiative corrections contributing to the anomalous spin magnetic moment of the electron. Solid lines indicate electrons and dashed lines indicate photons or the external magnetic field. Diagrams I give order α radiative corrections; diagrams II give α^2 corrections.

III. Atomic g_J-values

The theory of atomic magnetism for a multielectron atom is based on a generalized Dirac-Breit equation with the addition of a term to represent the interaction of the anomalous spin magnetic moment of each electron with the external magnetic field.[7] The equation reads:

$$\left\{ \sum_{k=1}^{n} [\beta_k\, mc^2 + \boldsymbol{\alpha}_k \cdot (c\mathbf{p}_k + e\mathbf{A}_k)] + V + \sum_{l>k=1}^{n} B_{kl} + \Omega_{H_0} \right\} \Psi = E\Psi \qquad (2)$$

E is the stationary state energy, including the rest energy of the n electrons; V is the sum of the electrostatic interactions:

$$V = -\sum_{k=1}^{n} \frac{Ze^2}{r_k} + \sum_{l>k=1}^{n} \frac{e^2}{r_{kl}} \qquad (2a)$$

in which $-e$ is the electron charge, Ze is the nuclear charge; $\mathbf{p}_k$ is the momentum of the kth electron; $\mathbf{A}_k$ is the vector potential of the external field at the kth electron and for a field $\mathbf{H}_0$ constant in space and time,

$$\mathbf{A}_k = 1/2\, \mathbf{H}_0 \times \mathbf{r}_k; \tag{2b}$$

$\boldsymbol{\alpha}_k$, β_k are the Dirac matrices; B_{kl} is the Breit interaction between the kth and lth electrons,

$$B_{kl} = \frac{-e^2}{2r_{kl}}\left[\boldsymbol{\alpha}_k\cdot\boldsymbol{\alpha}_l + \frac{(\boldsymbol{\alpha}_k\cdot\mathbf{r}_{kl})(\boldsymbol{\alpha}_l\cdot\mathbf{r}_{kl})}{r_{kl}^2}\right] \tag{2c}$$

in which $\mathbf{r}_{kl} = \mathbf{r}_k - \mathbf{r}_l$;

$$\Omega_{H_0} = \mu_0\left(\frac{\alpha}{2\pi} - 0.328\frac{\alpha^2}{\pi^2}\right)\sum_{k=1}^{n}\boldsymbol{\sigma}_k'\cdot\mathbf{H}_0 \tag{2d}$$

is the interaction of the anomalous part of the electron spin magnetic moments with the external field $\mathbf{H}_0$, in which $\boldsymbol{\sigma}_k'$ is the 4×4 Pauli spin matrix; the wave function Ψ depends on n space coordinates $\mathbf{r}_k$ and on n 4-component spinor variables.

The magnetic interaction term linear in H_0 is computed with first-order perturbation theory by evaluating the diagonal matrix element of:

$$\mathcal{H}_{H_0} = \sum_{k=1}^{n} e\boldsymbol{\alpha}_k\cdot\mathbf{A}_k + \Omega_{H_0} \tag{3}$$

for the zeroth order wavefunction Ψ_0 obtained from Eq. (2) with the omission of the Hamiltonian terms (3) which depend on the magnetic field. Another equivalent procedure is to derive a Schroedinger-Pauli equation from Eq. (2) and then to evaluate by first-order perturbation theory the energy term which depends linearly on H_0. Higher-order terms in H_0 correspond to diamagnetic corrections and are usually negligible. The result for the magnetic interaction energy can be expressed:

$$E_{H_0} = \mu_0 g_J H_0 M_J \tag{4}$$

in which M_J is the magnetic quantum number for the total electronic angular momentum. The quantity g_J can be expressed as a power series in α and the calculations are correct to the order of α^2.

The lowest order term for g_J is the value obtained from the Schroedinger-Pauli theory. If the atom obeys Russell-Saunders coupling so that the total orbital angular momentum **L** and the total spin angular momentum **S** are separately constants of the motion, then

$$g_J = g_L \frac{J(J+1)+L(L+1)-S(S+1)}{2J(J+1)} + g_S \frac{J(J+1)+S(S+1)-L(L+1)}{2J(J+1)} \tag{5}$$

in which $g_L = 1$ and $g_S = 2$. If the atom obeys the jj coupling scheme then the atomic magnetic moment results from the coupling of all the electronic magnetic moments characterized by their g_{J_i} values. For the simple case of two electrons with jj coupling

$$g_J = g_{j_1} \frac{J(J+1)+j_1(j_1+1)-j_2(j_2+1)}{2J(J+1)} + g_{j_2} \frac{J(J+1)+j_2(j_2+1)-j_1(j_1+1)}{2J(J+1)} \tag{6}$$

in which j_1 and j_2 are the angular momentum quantum numbers for the two electrons.

For many of the atoms studied the Russell-Saunders coupling is a good approximation. However, slight deviations from this coupling scheme cause important perturbations in the theoretical g_J values from the viewpoint of high precision measurements. If several states with the same configuration and the same total angular momentum quantum number J are present, the spin-orbit interactions lead to an admixture of these states and hence to an alteration in the g_J value obtained for a pure LS state. An example is the oxygen atom[9] for which the ground state electronic configuration is $1s^2 2s^2 2p^4$, and two of the LS states, $^3P_2$ and $^1D_2$, are admixed by spin-orbit interactions. The amplitude c_k of the admixture of the foreign LS state is given by first-order perturbation theory as the matrix element of the spin-orbit interaction between the two states divided by the energy difference between the two states, and the change in g_J is $c_k^2 \Delta g$ in which Δg is the difference between g_J for the initial and final states. For the case of oxygen the admixture c_k of $^1D_2$ state with $^3P_2$ state is 0.0065, and the change in g_J for the $^3P_2$ state is -21×10^{-6}.

More generally, a combination of electrostatic interactions between electrons which leads to configuration mixing and of spin-orbit interactions can cause the admixture of states of different L and S and hence can alter the g_J value.[24] The amplitude c_k of the admixture of the foreign LS state is given by second-order perturbation theory as:

$$c_k = \frac{V_{0i}\xi_{ik}}{E_{0i}E_{0k}} \tag{7}$$

V_{0i} is the matrix element of the electrostatic interaction between the zeroth-order state 0 and the state i having a different configuration but the same L and S values. ξ_{ik} is the matrix element of the spin-orbit interaction between the state i and the state k which have the same configuration but different L, S values. E_{0i} and E_{0k} are the energy differences between states 0 and i and 0 and k, respectively. The corresponding change in g value is

$$\Delta g_J = \frac{V_{0i}^2 \xi_{ik}^2 \Delta g}{E_{0i}^2 E_{0k}^2} \tag{8}$$

in which $\Delta g = g_{J(k)} - g_{J(0)}$. As an example, consider Na in its ground state with the zeroth-order configuration $1s^2 2s^2 2p^6 3s$, $^2S_{\frac{1}{2}}$. State i can be a configuration $1s^2 2s^2 2p^5 3s 3p$, $^2S_{\frac{1}{2}}$ and state k can then be a $^2P_{\frac{1}{2}}$ or $^4P_{\frac{1}{2}}$ state. In Na the fractional change in g_J is estimated to be about 1 part in a million; the changes in g_J are larger for the heavier alkalis, and for Cs it is about 7 parts in 10^5.

The effect of virtual radiative corrections is taken into account by using instead of $g_s = 2$, the value given in Eq. (1) from the quantum electrodynamical calculation for the scattering of a free electron by an external magnetic field:

$$g_s = 2 \left[1 + \frac{\alpha}{2\pi} - 0.328 \frac{\alpha^2}{\pi^2} \right] = 2(1.0011596)$$

Relativistic contributions to the magnetic interaction energy of order $\alpha^2 \mu_0 H_0$ arise from the Dirac-Breit equation (2). These contributions can be expressed[7] as the following expectation values:

$$\Delta E_R = -\frac{\mu_0}{2m^2 c^2} < U \left| \mathbf{H}_0 \cdot \sum_{k=1}^{n} (\mathbf{L}_k + \mathbf{\sigma}_k) \mathbf{p}_k^2 \right| U > \tag{9}$$

$$\Delta E_S = \frac{\mu_0}{2mc^2} < U \left| \sum_{k=1}^{n} \mathbf{\sigma}_k \cdot \nabla_k V \times \mathbf{A}_k \right| U > \tag{10}$$

$$\Delta E_B = \left\langle U \left| \sum_{l>k=1}^{n} \left\{ -\frac{e}{2mc^2} \frac{e^2}{r_{kl}} \left[\mathbf{A}_k \cdot \left(1 + \frac{\mathbf{r}_{kl}\mathbf{r}_{kl}}{r_{kl}^2} \right) \cdot \frac{\mathbf{p}_l}{mc} + \mathbf{A}_l \cdot \left(1 + \frac{\mathbf{r}_{kl}\mathbf{r}_{kl}}{r_{kl}^2} \right) \cdot \frac{\mathbf{p}_k}{mc} \right] + \right. \right. $$

$$\left. \left. + \frac{\mu_0 e^2}{mc^2 r_{kl}^3} (\mathbf{\sigma}_k \cdot \mathbf{r}_{kl} \times \mathbf{A}_l + \mathbf{\sigma}_l \cdot \mathbf{r}_{lk} \times \mathbf{A}_k) \right\} \right| U \right\rangle \tag{11}$$

$\mathbf{p}_k$, $\mathbf{L}_k$, $\boldsymbol{\sigma}_k 2$ are the linear momentum, orbital angular momentum, and spin angular momentum operators for the kth electron; V is the electrostatic potential energy and $\mathbf{A}_k$ is the vector potential at the position $\mathbf{r}_k$ of the kth electron; $\mathbf{r}_{kl} = \mathbf{r}_k - \mathbf{r}_l$; U is the normalized wavefunction which satisfies the Schroedinger-Pauli approximation equation:

$$\left\{ V + \sum_{k=1}^{n} \left(\frac{\mathbf{p}_k{}^2}{2m} - \frac{\mathbf{p}_k{}^4}{8m^3c^2} - \frac{i\hbar}{4mc} \boldsymbol{\sigma}_k \cdot \nabla_k V R_k) \right) - \right.$$

$$\left. \frac{-mc^2}{4} \sum_{l>k=1}^{n} (R_k R_l M_{kl} + M_{kl} R_k R_l + R_k M_{kl} R_l + R_l M_{kl} R_k) \right\} U = WU \tag{12}$$

$$R_k = \frac{\boldsymbol{\sigma}_k \cdot \mathbf{p}_k}{mc}; \quad M_{kl} = \frac{e^2}{2mc^2 r_{kl}} \left(\boldsymbol{\sigma}_k \cdot \boldsymbol{\sigma}_l + \frac{\boldsymbol{\sigma}_k \cdot \mathbf{r}_{kl} \boldsymbol{\sigma}_l \cdot \mathbf{r}_{kl}}{r_{kl}{}^2} \right); \quad W = E - nmc^2$$

The contributions ΔE_R, ΔE_S, and ΔE_B are of the order $\alpha^2 \mu_0 H_0$ and correspond to familiar contributions to fine structure of order $\alpha^2 r_y$. Such a correspondence is to be expected in view of the occurrence of $\mathbf{A}_k$ in the Dirac-Breit equation (2) only in the combination $\mathbf{p}_k + (e/c)\mathbf{A}_k$. Since this combination occurs also in the classical Hamiltonian and equations of motion for electrons, the effect of a given external vector potential can be regarded as inducing the diamagnetic momentum $(e/c)\mathbf{A}_k$ in electron k to give it the total momentum $\mathbf{p}_k + (e/c)\mathbf{A}_k$. A general diamagnetic classical interpretation for magnetic interaction energies is thus possible. For example, the usual nonrelativistic contribution of order $\mu_0 H_0$ has the well-known classical interpretation of diamagnetically-induced kinetic energy due to the product of mechanical momentum $\mathbf{p}$ and the diamagnetically induced momentum $e\mathbf{A}/c$ ($\mathbf{p}$ may be taken as the original momentum for $\mathbf{A} = 0$ if $e\mathbf{A}/c \ll \mathbf{p}$). The contribution ΔE_R of Eq. (9) to $\alpha^2 \mu_0 H_0$ is due to the "relativistic increase of mass" in which one factor of the fourth power momentum term is diamagnetically induced momentum. The contribution ΔE_S of Eq. (10) has the classical spin-orbit energy explanation with $e\mathbf{A}/c$ replacing $\mathbf{p}$. The contribution ΔE_B of Eq. (11) corresponds to the spin k-orbit l and to the orbit-orbit interaction energies with $e\mathbf{A}/c$ replacing $\mathbf{p}$. From this point of view it is clear that spin-spin contributions to fine structure have no analogous $\alpha^2 \mu_0 H_0$ contributions. Accurate evaluation of ΔE_R, ΔE_S, and ΔE_B requires a knowledge of the

Schroedinger wavefunction both as to its dependence on angular and radial variables.

The nucleus of the atom is treated as a point charge Ze of infinite mass in the Dirac-Breit equation. The effects of the nuclear mass, size, and moments can be treated by perturbation theory. The effect of the finite mass of the nucleus[10] is obtained from the Schroedinger-Pauli equation by including terms for the total momentum of the nucleus and of each electron of the form $\mathbf{p} - (q/c)\mathbf{A}$ in which $\mathbf{p}$ is the linear kinetic momentum of the particle and $\mathbf{A}$ is the vector potential $(\mathbf{A} = (\mathbf{H}_0 \times \mathbf{r}/2))$ for a uniform applied field $\mathbf{H}_0$, $\mathbf{r}$ = position coordinate with respect to a fixed point, q = charge of particle. The coordinates of the center of mass of the atom can be separated out, and the following Hamiltonian magnetic interaction term is obtained due to the nuclear motion:

$$\mathcal{H} = \frac{e}{2mc}\left(-\frac{m}{M}\right)\left\{\sum_{k=1}^{n}(\mathbf{s}_k \times \mathbf{p}_k)\cdot\mathbf{H}_0 + \sum_{j \neq k}(\mathbf{s}_j \times \mathbf{p}_k + \mathbf{s}_k \times \mathbf{p}_j)\cdot\mathbf{H}_0\right\} \quad (13)$$

$\mathbf{p}_k$ = linear momentum of kth electron; $\mathbf{s}_k = \mathbf{r}_k - \mathbf{r}_N$ in which $\mathbf{r}_N$ = radius vector for the nucleus; M = mass of nucleus. The first term in Eq. (13) is a simple reduced mass correction to the interaction of the orbital magnetic moment of the electrons with the external magnetic field. The second term involves a cross product between position and momentum coordinates of two different electrons and corresponds to the "specific isotope shift" or the Hughes-Eckart effect in atomic optical spectra. These effects of the nuclear mass are of order $(m/M)\mu_0 H_0$.

The finite size of the nucleus and the nuclear magnetic dipole and electric quadrupole moments alter the Schroedinger atomic wavefunction obtained for a point charge nucleus, and admixture of states with different g_J values can occur.[11] Furthermore, the change of the nuclear electrostatic potential due to the finite nuclear size or the nuclear electric quadrupole moment will alter the relativistic contributions to the magnetic interaction. These effects are much smaller than the present experimental errors. For a mu-mesonic atom, however, the radius of an atom with large Z is of the order of the nuclear radius, and the size of the nucleus will influence appreciably the value of the atomic magnetic moment. Precise measurements of the magnetic moments of mu-mesonic atoms, which are now possible, may thus yield useful information about nuclear structure.[25]

MEASUREMENTS OF ATOMIC MAGNETISM

IV. Free Electron

Considerations based on the uncertainty principle emphasize the difficulties of experiments to measure the spin magnetic moment of the free electron by classical type experiments, e.g. a magnetometer or a Stern-Gerlach experiment.[12,13] Of the many attempts to measure the electron spin magnetic moment by quantum-mechanical type experiments, two experiments have been successful thus far, but their accuracy is considerably less than that obtained in measurements of atomic magnetic moments.

The spin magnetic moment of the free electron was first measured in an experiment which utilized Mott scattering for the production and analysis of the electron polarization and compared the electron spin precession frequency to the electron orbital cyclotron frequency.[13] A schematic diagram of the apparatus is shown in Fig. 2. The incoming

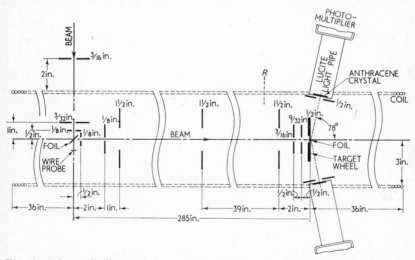

Fig. 2. Schematic diagram of apparatus to determine the electron spin magnetic moment by use of Mott scattering for production and analysis of the electron polarization.

electron beam of (420 ± 0.8)kev energy is obtained from a Cockroft-Walton generator. Mott scattering at 90° by a gold foil produces a partial polarization for the scattered beam transverse to the direction of the scattering. In the longitudinal magnetic field produced by a solenoid the electron spin precesses at the rate $\nu_s = (g_s \mu_0 H_0)/h$. At

F

the position of the analyzing foil the orientation of the electron spin is determined from a study of the asymmetry in azimuthal angle of the electron scattering. Approximately 5 revolutions of the electron spin are obtained between the first and second scatterers in the field of 400 gauss. The magnetic field is measured by the cyclotron orbital frequency $\nu_l = (2g_l\mu_0 H_0/h)$ with use being made of the focusing property of the orbital motion at integral numbers of revolutions. Relativistic corrections to ν_s and ν_l cancel in the ratio ν_s/ν_l to a sufficient accuracy. The result of the experiment is $g_s = 2.00 \pm 0.01$, where the error is due primarily to inaccuracy in the determination of the spin orientation by the analyzer.

A spin resonance experiment on electrons in a plasma has recently been achieved using optical methods for the production and detection of the electron polarization.[14] A schematic diagram of the experimental arrangement is shown in Fig. 3. Sodium atoms at a partial pressure

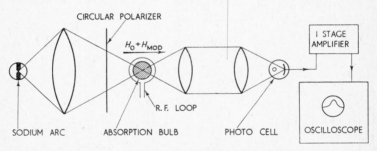

Fig. 3. Schematic diagram of experimental arrangement to determine the electron spin magnetic moment by use of polarized light to produce and detect the electron polarization.

of about 10^{-7} mm Hg and argon at a pressure of 70 mm Hg are contained in a bulb and illuminated with circularly polarized sodium resonance radiation. A net polarization of the sodium atoms is produced thereby. Periodically a discharge is excited to produce an electron density of some 3×10^8 electrons/cm³, and the electrons become polarized by exchange collisions with the polarized sodium atoms. In a magnetic field H_0 an electron spin resonance transition can be induced by an rf magnetic field of frequency $\nu_s = \mu_0 g_s H_0/h$. The resulting change in net polarization then causes a change in polarization of the sodium atoms through the mechanism of electron exchange collisions. Since the transmission of polarized sodium resonance radiation through the sodium atoms depends on the amount of polarization of the sodium atoms, the electron spin resonance can be detected by the resulting change in light transmission. The width of the electron spin resonance is largely determined by the electron spin polarization relaxation associated with electron-argon collisions. A Zeeman transition $\Delta M_F = \pm 1$ in the $F = 2$ hyperfine structure level of the ground state of sodium can be induced in the magnetic field H_0 also, and detected by the change in light transmission. The result of the experiment is the ratio of the spin g value of the electron g_s to the value $g_J(\mathrm{Na},^2S_{\frac{1}{2}})$,

$$g_s/g_J(Na,^2S_{\frac{1}{2}}) = 0.999974 \pm 0.00003$$

in which the error is due to electron spin relaxation processes and inhomogeneity of the magnetic field.

V. Hydrogen

The most precise value for the electron spin magnetic moment is obtained from a comparison of a Zeeman transition frequency in the ground state of H and the cyclotron orbital frequency of a free electron in the same magnetic field. This comparison of $g_J(\mathrm{H},^2S_{\frac{1}{2}})$ to g_l has been obtained by two experiments. One is a measurement of $g_J(\mathrm{H},^2S_{\frac{1}{2}})/g_p$, in which g_p, the g-value for a proton, is obtained from a proton resonance absorption experiment; the second is a measurement of g_l/g_p.

The hyperfine energy levels of the ground state of hydrogen in a magnetic field are shown in Fig. 4, and the energy levels are given by the Breit-Rabi formula:

$$W_{F=J\pm\frac{1}{2},M} = \mu_0 g_p H_0 M \pm \frac{\Delta W}{2} [1 + 2Mx + x^2]^{\frac{1}{2}} \tag{14}$$

where F is the quantum number for total angular momentum and M is the associated magnetic quantum number; ΔW is the energy difference at zero magnetic field between the $F = 1$ and $F = 0$ hyperfine levels; $x = \mu_0(g_J - g_p)H_0/\Delta W$.

One measurement of $g_J(\mathrm{H},^2S_{\frac{1}{2}})/g_p$ was done by the atomic beam magnetic resonance method.[11] The transition $(F, M) = (1,0) \leftrightarrow (1, -1)$ was observed in a magnetic field near 1430 gauss at a frequency of about 3655 Mc/sec. With extensive shimming of the magnetic C-field the natural line width of 60 kc/sec corresponding to a 4 cm rf transition region was obtained. A proton resonance absorption measurement was made in the same magnetic field. Since the hfs energy difference is known from atomic beam and microwave absorption experiments to an accuracy of about 0.1 ppm,[15] the above experiment determines $g_J(\mathrm{H},^2S_{\frac{1}{2}})/g_p$. Due to diamagnetic shielding the magnetic field at the

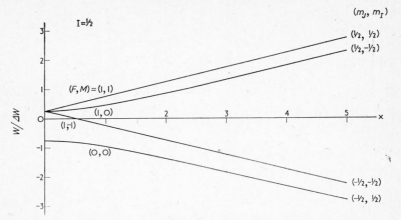

Fig. 4. Energy levels of the ground state of hydrogen in a magnetic field.

protons differs slightly from the applied magnetic field and hence in the measured ratio $g_J(\mathrm{H},^2S_{\frac{1}{2}})/g_p$, g_p should be interpreted as the g-value of protons in the sample used, which was a spherical sample of mineral oil. An accuracy of ± 1 ppm was obtained for $g_J(\mathrm{H},^2S_{\frac{1}{2}})/g_p$.

A measurement of $g_J(\mathrm{H},^2S_{\frac{1}{2}})/g_p$ has also been made by a microwave magnetic resonance absorption method using hydrogen gas.[16] The experimental arrangement is shown in Fig. 5. Hydrogen atoms formed

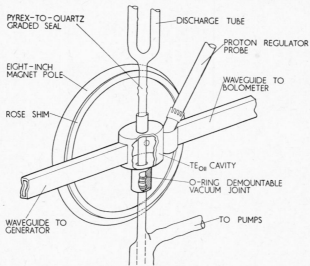

Fig. 5. Cutaway view of apparatus used for microwave magnetic resonance absorption experiments.

in a discharge tube diffuse through a high Q microwave cavity placed between the pole faces of an electromagnet. Fixed frequency microwave power is fed into the cavity whose TE_{011} mode is such as to have a component of H_{rf} perpendicular to the static magnetic field H_0 of the electromagnet. If the static magnetic field is at the resonant value for a transition $\Delta M = \pm 1$ in hydrogen, microwave power transmitted to the bolometer will be reduced. At a frequency of about 9000 Mc/sec, the resonant magnetic fields for the two transitions with $\Delta m_J = \pm 1$, $\Delta m_I = 0$ were observed with a line width of about 200 kc/sec, which was due to magnetic field inhomogeneity and collision broadening. The proton resonance absorption frequency for a mineral oil sample was measured in the same static magnetic field so the ratio $g_J(H,^2S_{\frac{1}{2}})/g_p$ is determined. A statistical accuracy of ± 0.3 ppm was obtained.

The orbital cyclotron frequency of the free electron has been compared with the proton resonance absorption frequency in two independent experiments. In the first[17] the electrons were obtained from a hot filament and the electron cyclotron resonance was observed by its effect on the electron trajectories. In the second[18] the electrons were obtained by the photoelectric effect and the resonance was observed by a microwave absorption method. The sources of error in these measurements arise from inhomogeneity and nonconstancy of the magnetic field, diamagnetic effects, space charge effects, and the relativistic dependence of mass on velocity. The accuracy for each of these measurements is about ± 10 ppm.

Combination of the average experimental values of $g_J(H,^2S_{\frac{1}{2}})/g_p$ and g_l/g_p yields the result:

$$\frac{g_J(H,^2S_{\frac{1}{2}})}{g_l} = 2[1.001139 \pm 0.000010]$$

Use of the theoretical relativistic contributions ΔE_R and ΔE_S of Eqs. (9) and (10) gives the relation:

$$g_J(H,^2S_{\frac{1}{2}}) = g_s(1 - \alpha^2/3) = g_s(1 - 17.7 \times 10^{-6})$$

Hence the experimentally determined value of g_s/g_l is

$$g_s/g_l = 2[1.001156 \pm 0.000010]$$

This experimental value is in agreement with the theoretical value $g_s/g_l = 2[1.0011596]$, but it is not sufficiently accurate to test the fourth-order α^2 radiative correction to the spin magnetic moment of the electron.

To ascertain experimentally that the g_J value of hydrogen does not depend significantly on nuclear properties, the electron g value in the ground state of deuterium $g_J(D,^2S_{\frac{1}{2}})$ has been measured. An early measurement by the atomic beam magnetic resonance method compared directly $g_J(D,^2S_{\frac{1}{2}})$ with $g_J(H,^2S_{\frac{1}{2}})$ and found them to be equal to within the experimental error of ± 10 ppm.[19] A recent measurement by the microwave magnetic resonance absorption method of $g_J(D,^2S_{\frac{1}{2}})/g_p$ again yielded $g_J(D,^2S_{\frac{1}{2}})/g_J(H,^2S_{\frac{1}{2}}) = 1$ to within the experimental accuracy of 1 ppm.[20]

VI. Other Atoms

Accurate measurements have been made of g_J values of many atoms by the methods of radiofrequency and microwave spectroscopy. Although some of the earlier measurements on multielectron atoms were used for the determination of g_s/g_l for the electron, at present g_J values for multielectron atoms are used primarily to test the theory of relativistic contributions to atomic magnetism or to provide a criterion for the excellence of an atomic wavefunction.

The g_J value of the two electron system in the $1s2s,^3S_1$ metastable state of helium has been studied particularly carefully both experimentally and theoretically. In an atomic beam magnetic resonance experiment the transitions $\Delta M = \pm 1, \pm 2$ in helium and the transition $(F,M) = (1,0) \leftrightarrow (1,-1)$ in hydrogen were observed in the same magnetic field, and thus the ratio $g_J(He,^3S_1)/g_J(H,^2S_{\frac{1}{2}})$ was determined. The first such experiment[21] used a transition region with a single oscillating field and determined the ratio to an accuracy of ± 16 ppm. The method of separated oscillating fields was used in a more recent experiment[8] and allowed the achievement of narrow natural line widths despite the presence of magnetic field inhomogeneities in the C-region. A schematic diagram of the apparatus used for the latter experiment is given in Fig. 6. A block diagram of the radiofrequency system is shown in Fig. 7. The "hairpin" arrangement for the separated oscillating fields is shown in Fig. 8. Line shapes for hydrogen and helium transitions obtained by the method of separated oscillating fields are shown in Figs. 9 and 10. For hydrogen, only transitions between the two levels $(F,M) = (1,0)$ and $(1,-1)$ are involved. For helium all three Zeeman levels $M = 0, \pm 1$ are involved. Theoretical line shapes for the three-level case near the central resonance are shown in Fig. 11. The experimental value obtained is

$$\frac{g_J(He,^3S_1)}{g_J(H,^2S_{\frac{1}{2}})} = 1-(23.3 \pm 0.8) \times 10^{-6}$$

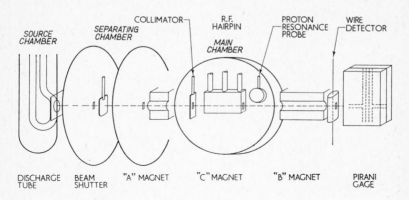

THE ATOMIC BEAM APPARATUS

Fig. 6. Schematic diagram of atomic beam magnetic resonance apparatus used for measurement of $g_J(\mathrm{He},^3S_1)/g_J(\mathrm{H},^2S_{\frac{1}{2}})$.

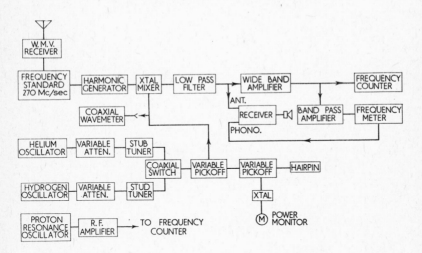

BLOCK DIAGRAM OF THE RADIO FREQUENCY SYSTEM

Fig. 7. Block diagram of the radiofrequency system used for measurement of $g_J(\mathrm{He},^3S_1)/g_J(\mathrm{H},^2S_{\frac{1}{2}})$.

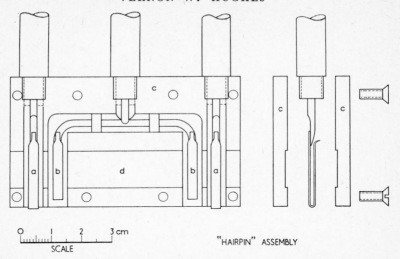

"HAIRPIN" ASSEMBLY

Fig. 8. Construction of separated oscillating fields system. The parts labelled "b" are loops made of Cu; they are fed from a single rf source and carry the rf currents which produce the separated oscillating fields. The parts labelled "a" are auxiliary Cu loops used for producing two independent single oscillating fields, which allow measurement of the magnetic field in the neighborhood of both "b" loops. The brass plates "c" serve as rf shields for the loops and also as the outer conductor for the coaxial line feeding the loops. The beam passes parallel to the groove "d". At the right of the figure an end view along the propagation direction of the beam is shown.

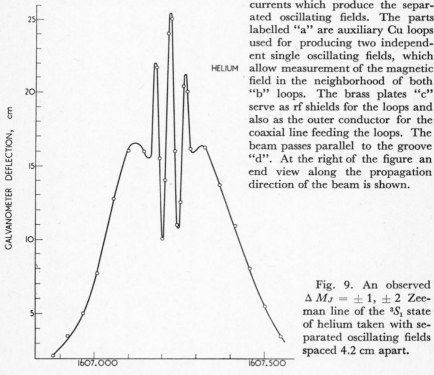

HELIUM

Fig. 9. An observed $\Delta M_J = \pm 1, \pm 2$ Zeeman line of the $^3S_1$ state of helium taken with separated oscillating fields spaced 4.2 cm apart.

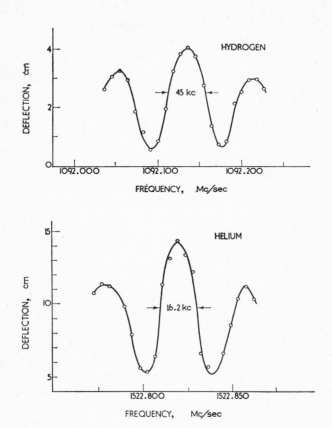

Fig. 10. Central, "near resonance" portions of Zeeman lines for hydrogen and helium taken with separated oscillating fields spaced 4.2 cm apart. For hydrogen the transition observed was $(F, M) = (1, 0) \leftrightarrow (1, -1)$ in the ground $^2S_{\frac{1}{2}}$ state; the amplitude of the radiofrequency field was adjusted to give maximum intensity at resonance. For helium the transition observed was $\Delta M_J = \pm 1, \pm 2$ in the metastable $^3S_1$ state (i.e. any transition in which M_J changes for any of the three M_J states); the amplitude of the radiofrequency field was adjusted to be about 60% of the value which gives maximum intensity at resonance.

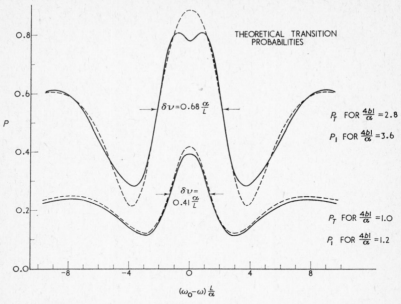

Fig. 11. Theoretical transition probabilities near resonance for Zeeman transitions in the $^3S_1$ state of helium by the method of separated oscillating fields, averaged over the velocity distribution in the beam. P_1 is the probability of a transition from the initial magnetic substate $M_J = +1$ to either of the magnetic substates $M_J = 0$ or $M_J = -1$; P_T is the probability of a transition from any of the magnetic substates $M_J = 0$, $+1$, or -1 to a different magnetic substate. α = most probable velocity of atoms in the source; L = distance between oscillating fields; l = length of each oscillating field; b is the matrix element for the transition $\Delta M_J = \pm 1$ divided by $\hbar$ and it is proportional to the amplitude of the oscillating field (the two oscillating fields have the same amplitude and phase); $\delta\nu$ is the frequency width at half height between the peak and first minimum; $\omega_0 = \mu_0 g_J H_0/\hbar$; ω = applied angular frequency. The cases $(4bl/\alpha) = 3.6$ and $(4bl/\alpha) = 2.8$ correspond to conditions for maximum transition probability at exact resonance for P_1 and P_T, respectively.

The theoretical value for $g_J(\text{He},{}^3S_1)$ is given by:

$$g_J(\text{He},{}^3S_1) = 2\left[1 + \frac{\alpha}{2\pi} - 0.328\,\frac{\alpha^2}{\pi^2} - \frac{1}{3}\frac{\langle T\rangle}{mc^2} - \frac{1}{6}\frac{\langle e^2/r_{12}\rangle}{mc^2}\right] \tag{15}$$

$$= 2[1 + 1161.4\times10^{-6} - 1.8\times10^{-6} - 38.7\times10^{-6} - 2.3\times10^{-6}]$$

$$= 2[1.0011186]$$

The two terms involving α constitute the virtual radiative correction to the spin magnetic moment of the electron. The term $-\frac{1}{3}(\langle T\rangle/mc^2)$

in which $\langle T \rangle$ is the expectation value for the kinetic energy of the two electrons, arises from the relativistic contributions ΔE_R and ΔE_S of Eqs. (9) and (10). The term $-\frac{1}{6}(<e^2/r_{12}>/mc^2)$ arises from the relativistic contribution ΔE_B of Eq. (11). The theoretical value for $g_J(\mathrm{H},{}^2S_{\frac{1}{2}})$ is given by:

$$g_J(\mathrm{H},{}^2S_{\frac{1}{2}}) = 2\left[1+\frac{\alpha}{2\pi} - 0.328\,\frac{\alpha^2}{\pi^2} - \frac{\alpha^2}{3}\right] \tag{16}$$

Hence,

$$\frac{g_J(\mathrm{He},{}^3S_1)}{g_J(\mathrm{H},{}^2S_{\frac{1}{2}})_{\text{theor}}} = 1 - (23.3 \pm 1.0) \times 10^{-6}$$

in which the uncertainty in the theoretical value is estimated from the neglected radiative effects of order $\alpha^3\mu_0H_0$. The excellent agreement between the experimental and theoretical values provides strong confirmation of the theory of relativistic contributions to atomic magnetism as based on the Dirac-Breit equation up to order $\alpha^2\mu_0H_0$. Furthermore, the "additivity" of the anomalous magnetic moments of the two electrons as treated in Eq. (2) is confirmed. The comparison of the g_J values for He and H does not provide any test of the anomalous magnetic moment of the electron, because this contribution cancels in the ratio $g_J(\mathrm{He},{}^3S_1)/g_J(\mathrm{H},{}^2S_{\frac{1}{2}})$. Theoretically, it remains to justify the use of Eq. (2) for helium by a more fundamental field theoretical approach involving the use of the Bethe-Salpeter equation for two electrons in the presence of the nuclear Coulomb field.[22]

Another carefully studied atom is oxygen in its ground configuration $2p^4$ for both fine structure states ${}^3P_2$ and ${}^3P_1$. The experimental values were obtained by the microwave magnetic resonance absorption method.[23] Figure 12 shows a resonance line for the transition $M_J = 0 \leftrightarrow M_J = 1$ in the ${}^3P_2$ state at a frequency of 9100 Mc/sec. The oxygen resonance frequencies are compared with the proton resonance frequency. Use of the measured value of $g_J(\mathrm{H},{}^2S_{\frac{1}{2}})/g_p$ and the theoretical value for $g_J(\mathrm{H},{}^2S_{\frac{1}{2}})$ determines the results:

$$g_J(\mathrm{O},{}^3P_1)_{\text{expt.}} = 1.500986 \pm .000002$$
$$g_J(\mathrm{O},{}^3P_2)_{\text{expt.}} = 1.500921 \pm .000002$$

The various contributions to the theoretical oxygen g_J values are shown in Table 1, and the resulting theoretical values are:[26]

$$g_J(\mathrm{O},{}^3P_1)_{\text{theor.}} = 1.500995$$
$$g_J(\mathrm{O},{}^3P_2)_{\text{theor.}} = 1.500931$$

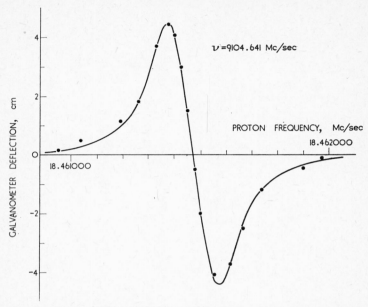

Fig. 12. An observed $M_J = 1 \leftrightarrow M_J = 0$ line in the microwave magnetic resonance spectrum of the $^3P_2$ ground state of atomic oxygen. The apparatus records what is essentially the derivative of the absorption line. The observed points have been fitted with a theoretical curve which corresponds to a Lorentz absorption line having a half width of 5 parts in 10^6.

TABLE 1

THEORETICAL g_J VALUES FOR THE $2p^4$, $^3P_1$ AND $^3P_2$ TERMS OF OXYGEN

Contribution	Δg_1	Δg_2
	(Units of 10^{-6})	
Departure from LS coupling	0	−21
Virtual radiative effect	+1160	+1160
$\Delta E_R + \Delta E_S + \Delta E_B$	−167	−210
Motion of nucleus	+2	+2
Total	+995	+931

$\Delta g_1 (\Delta g_2)$ are the contributions to the g_J value of the $^3P_1(^3P_2)$ state of O. Hence $g_J(^3P_1) = 1.500995$ and $g_J(^3P_2) = 1.500931$.

Both experimental values are lower than the corresponding theoretical values by 7 parts in 10^6. The experimental and theoretical values for the differences $g_J(^3P_2) - g_J(^3P_1)$ agree within the experimental error. The most likely cause for the discrepancies between the experimental and theoretical g_J values is inaccuracy in the atomic wavefunction used for the computation of the relativisitc contributions ΔE_R and ΔE_S. It should be noted, however, that computations of ΔE_R with several different wavefunctions yielded values considerably closer than could account for the discrepancies.

The g_J values for the alkali atoms have been measured and the theoretical g_J values for these single valence electron atoms have been computed. Substantial discrepancies exist between the experimental and theoretical g_J values for Cs and Rb. The breakdown of Russell-Saunders coupling due to a combination of electrostatic and spin-orbit interactions produces appreciable positive contributions to the theoretical g_J values, which is difficult to calculate accurately and which may be capable of accounting for the discrepancies.*,24

Table 2 (page 87 et seq.) summarizes the experimental and theoretical information on atomic g_J values.

In conclusion, the excellent agreement between the experimental and theoretical values of $g_J(\mathrm{He},^3S_1)/g_J(\mathrm{H},^2S_{\frac{1}{2}})$ provides strong support for the theory of atomic magnetism based on the generalized Dirac-Breit equation with the addition of a magnetic interaction term for the anomalous electron spin magnetic moments. Several atomic g_J values involving both orbital and spin contributions are known sufficiently well experimentally so that g_s/g_l for the electron could be

---

* W. Perl, *Phys. Rev.* **91**, 852 (1953). Relativistic contributions to the g_J values of alkali atoms are calculated in this reference. The general theory of these contributions to the g_J value of any atom and its specialization to alkali atoms in Eq. (33) are correct. However, a calculational error was made in evaluating ΔE_R and ΔE_S. The error first appears in Eq. (42), which should read

$$\left\langle \frac{z_{1i}^2}{r_{1i}^3} \right\rangle = \frac{1}{3} \left\langle \frac{1}{r_1} \right\rangle \tag{42}$$

correct to terms of relative order r_i^2/r_1^2. . Evaluation of ΔE_{RSB} can be made directly from Eq. (33) using an effective central potential for V defined by the effective quantum numbers in Perl's paper. The result is that in Table 1 the quantities $(\Delta g/2)_+$ are identically zero and $\Delta g/2$ is given by:

$$\frac{\Delta g}{2} = \left(\frac{\Delta g}{2} \right)_M + \left(\frac{\Delta g}{2} \right)_L$$

The values for $(\Delta g/2)_M$ and $(\Delta g/2)_L$ are correctly given in Table 1. The theoretical g_J values for alkali atoms given in Table 2 of the present paper incorporate this correction to Perl's paper. The error in Eq. (42) of Perl's paper also invalidates the numerical results given for ^2P states of Ga and In. Relativistic contributions are not included in our table for the theoretical g_J values of Ga and In.

obtained to an accuracy of 1 part in a million, if adequate atomic wave-functions were available. Such an accuracy would represent an improvement by a factor of 10 over the accuracy with which g_s/g_l is known from experiments on hydrogen and the free electron. Alternatively, the theoretical quantum electrodynamic radiative corrections to the electron spin magnetic moment up to order α^2 can be regarded as correct, and then accurate experimental atomic g_J values can be used as a test for atomic wavefunctions.

REFERENCES

[1] W. E. Lamb, Jr. and R. C. Retherford, *Phys. Rev.* **72**, 241 (1947).

[2] J. E. Nafe and E. B. Nelson, *Phys. Rev.* **73**, 718 (1948).

[3] G. Breit, *Phys. Rev.* **72**, 984 (1947); J. Schwinger, *Phys. Rev.* **73**, 416 (1948).

[4] P. Kusch and H. M. Foley, *Phys. Rev.* **74**, 250 (1948).

[5] J. Schwinger, *Phys. Rev.* **76**, 790 (1949); R. Karplus and N. M. Kroll, *Phys. Rev.* **77**, 536 (1950); C. M. Sommerfield, *Phys. Rev.* **107**, 328 (1957), *Ann. Phys.* **5**, 26 (1958).

[6] Koenig, Prodell, and Kusch, *Phys. Rev.* **88**, 191 (1952); R. Beringer and M. A. Heald, *Phys. Rev.* **95**, 1474 (1954); J. H. Gardner, *Phys. Rev.* **83**, 996 (1951); P. Franken and S. Liebes, Jr., *Phys. Rev.* **104**, 1197 (1956).

[7] W. Perl and V. W. Hughes, *Phys. Rev.* **91**, 842 (1953); W. Perl, *Phys. Rev.* **91**, 852 (1953); A. Abragam and J. H. Van Vleck, *Phys. Rev.* **92**, 1448 (1953).

[8] Drake, Lurio, Hughes, and White, *Bull. Am. Phys. Soc.* II, **3**, 7 (1958), see article in *Phys. Rev.* (Dec., 1958).

[9] A. Abragam and J. H. Van Vleck, *Phys. Rev.* **92**, 1448 (1953).

[10] M. Phillips, *Phys. Rev.* **76**, 1803 (1949).

[11] Koenig, Prodell, and Kusch, *Phys. Rev.* **88**, 191 (1952).

[12] N. F. Mott and H. S. W. Massey, "The Theory of Atomic Collisions," Clarendon Press, Oxford, 1949.

[13] Louisell, Pidd, and Crane, *Phys. Rev.* **94**, 7 (1954).

[14] H. Dehmelt, *Phys. Rev.* **109**, 381 (1958).

[15] P. Kusch, *Phys. Rev.* **100**, 1188 (1955); J. P. Wittke and R. H. Dicke, *Phys. Rev.* **103**, 620 (1956).

[16] R. Beringer and M. A. Heald, *Phys. Rev.* **95**, 1474 (1954).

[17] J. H. Gardner, *Phys. Rev.* **83**, 996 (1951); J. H. Gardner and E. M. Purcell, *Phys. Rev.* **76**, 1262 (1949).

[18] P. Franken and S. Liebes, Jr., *Phys. Rev.* **104**, 1197 (1956).

[19] E. B. Nelson and J. E. Nafe, *Phys. Rev.* **76**, 1858 (1949).

[20] Geiger, Hughes, and Radford, *Phys. Rev.* **105**, 183 (1957).

[21] Hughes, Tucker, Rhoderick, and Weinreich, *Phys. Rev.* **91**, 828 (1953).

[22] E. E. Salpeter and H. A. Bethe, *Phys. Rev.* **84**, 1232 (1951); M. Gell-Mann and F. Low, *Phys. Rev.* **84**, 350 (1951); H. Araki, *Progress of Theoretical Physics* **17**, 619 (1957).

[23] E. B. Rawson and R. Beringer, *Phys. Rev.* **88**, 677 (1952); H. E. Radford and V. W. Hughes, *Bull. Am. Phys. Soc.* II, **3**, 8 (1958), see article in *Phys. Rev.* Dec., (1958).

[24] M. Phillips, *Phys. Rev.* **88**, 202 (1952).

[25] V. W. Hughes and V. L. Telegdi, *Bull. Am. Phys. Soc.* II, **3**, 229 (1958).

[26] F. R. Innes and C. W. Ufford, *Phys. Rev.* **111**, 194 (1958).

TABLE 2

Atom	State[b]	Quantity measured[i]	Experimental value[e]		Theoretical value[g]	Reference	
			$g_J/g_J(\text{H})$[c]	g_J[d]	g_J	Exper'l.	Theor'l.
electron	free	$\dfrac{g_s}{g_l}$		$g_s = 2.00 \pm 0.01$	$g_s = 2\left(1 + \dfrac{\alpha}{2\pi} - 0.328\dfrac{\alpha^2}{\pi^2}\right)$	54 L1	49 S1, 50 K1, 57 S1
		$\dfrac{g_s}{g_J(\text{Na})}$	0.999974(30)	2.00226(40)	$= 2.0023192$	58 D1	
H^1	$^2S_{\frac{1}{2}}$	$\dfrac{g_l}{g_p}$	$\dfrac{2g_l}{g_p} = 657.469(9)$[f]			51 G1, 56 F1	
		$\dfrac{g_J(\text{H})}{g_p}$	$\dfrac{g_J}{g_p} = 658.2176(0.8)$[f]	2.002277(10)	2.0022838	52 K1, 54 B1	28 B1, 40 M1
	$2^2S_{\frac{1}{2}}$	$\dfrac{g_J(\text{H})}{g_p}$	1.000016(12)	2.002309(16)	2.0023103	55 W1	28 B1, 40 M1
D^2	$^2S_{\frac{1}{2}}$	$\dfrac{g_J(\text{D})}{g_p}$	0.9999997(2.3)	2.002276(10)	2.0022838	49 N1, 57 G1	
		$\dfrac{g_J(\text{D})}{g_J(\text{H})}$					
He^4	$1s2\,^3S_1$	$\dfrac{g_J(\text{He})}{g_J(\text{H})}$	0.9999767(0.8)	2.002230(10)	2.0022373	53 H1, 58 D2	53 P1

TABLE 2—continued

Atom	State[b]	Quantity measured[i]	Experimental value[e] $g_J/g_J(H)$[c]	Experimental value[e] g_J[d]	Theoretical value[g] g_J	Reference Exper'l.	Reference Theor'l.
Li[6,7]	$^2S_{\frac{1}{2}}$	$\dfrac{g_J(Li)}{g_J(Na)}$	1.000016(25)	2.002309(27)	2.002297	49 K1	52 P1, 53 P2
N[14]	$^4S_{\frac{3}{2}}$	$\dfrac{g_J(N)}{g_p}$	0.9999184(1.7)	2.002114(10)	2.002	54 H1	
O[16]	$^3P_1$	$\dfrac{g_J(O)}{g_p}$	0.7496368(0.9)	1.500981(10)	1.500995	52 R1, 58 R1	53 A1, 54 K2, 58 I1
	$^3P_2$		0.7496043(0.9)	1.500916(10)	1.500931		
F[19]	$^2P_{\frac{3}{2}}$	$\dfrac{g_J(F)}{g_p}$	0.666170(2)	1.333857(11)	1.3341	58 R2	
Ne[20]	$2p^53s, {}^3P_2$	$\dfrac{g_J(Ne)}{g_J(He)}$	0.7495883(3)	1.500883(11)	1.50088	52 W1, 57 D1, 58 L1	
Na[23]	$^2S_{\frac{1}{2}}$	$\dfrac{g_J(Na)}{g_J(K)}$	1.000016(25)	2.002309(27)	2.002293	49 K1	52 P1, 53 P2
P[31]	$^4S_{\frac{3}{2}}$	$\dfrac{g_J(P)}{g_J(N)}$	0.99981(200)	2.0019(200)	2.002	55 D1	
A[40]	$3p^54s, {}^3P_2$	$\dfrac{g_J(A)}{g_J(He)}$	0.7496260(5)	1.500959(12)	1.5011	57 D1, 58 L1	

TABLE 2—continued

Atom	State[b]	Quantity measured[i]	Experimental value[e] $g_J/g_J(H)$[c]	g_J[d]	Theoretical value[g] g_J	Reference Exper'l.	Theor'l.
K^{39}	$^2S_{\frac{1}{2}}$	$\dfrac{g_J(K)}{g_J(H)}$	1.000016(4)	2.002309(11)	2.00230	52 F1	52 P1, 53 P2
Cr^{52}	$^7S_3$	$\dfrac{g_J(Cr)}{g_J(K)}$	0.999536(78)	2.001348(79)	2.002	53 B1	
$Cu^{63,65}$	$^2S_{\frac{1}{2}}$	$\dfrac{g_J(Cu)}{g_J(Cs)}$	1.00015(500)	2.0026(500)	2.002	57 T1	
$Ga^{69,71}$	$^2P_{\frac{1}{2}}$	$\dfrac{g_J(Ga,^2P_{\frac{1}{2}})}{g_J(Na)}$	0.332534(66)	0.665825(66)	0.66589	48 K1	52 P1, 53 P2
	$^2P_{\frac{3}{2}}$	$\dfrac{g_J(Ga,^2P_{\frac{3}{2}})}{g_J(Ga,^2P_{\frac{1}{2}})}$	0.666212(87)	1.333941(88)	1.33411		
Br	$^2P_{\frac{3}{2}}$	$\dfrac{g_J(Br,^2P_{\frac{3}{2}})}{g_J(Cl^{35},^2P_{\frac{3}{2}})}$ $= 0.9997(400)$				52 K2, 54 K1	
$Rb^{85,87}$	$^2S_{\frac{1}{2}}$	$\dfrac{g_J(Rb)}{g_J(Na)}$	1.000066(27)	2.002409(29)	2.00234	49 K1	52 P1, 53 P2
$Ag^{107,109}$	$^2S_{\frac{1}{2}}$	$\dfrac{g_J(Ag)}{g_J(Cs)}$	1.00002(105)	2.00232(105)	2.002	53 W1	
In^{115}	$^2P_{\frac{1}{2}}$	$\dfrac{g_J(In,^2P_{\frac{1}{2}})}{g_J(Na)}$	0.332531(102)	0.665819(104)	0.6659	50 M1, 48 K1	52 P1, 53 P2

G

TABLE 2—continued

Atom	State[b]	Quantity measured[i]	Experimental value[e]		Theoretical value[g]	Reference Exper'l. Theor'l.	
			$g_J/g_J(\text{H})$[c]	g_J[d]	g_J	Exper'l.	Theor'l.
	$^2P_{3/2}$	$\dfrac{g_J(\text{In},{}^2P_{3/2})}{g_J(\text{In},{}^2P_{1/2})}$	0.666392(120)	1.334301(12)	1.3341		
Xe[a]	$5p^56s\,{}^3P_2$	$\dfrac{g_J(\text{Xe},{}^3P_2)}{g_J(\text{He},{}^3S_1)}$	0.749593(60)	1.50089(60)		57 F1	
Cs^{133}	$^2S_{1/2}$	$\dfrac{g_J(\text{Cs})}{g_J(\text{Na})}$	1.000150(27)	2.002577(29)	2.00244	49 K1	52 P1, 53 P2
Pr^{141}	$^4I_{9/2}$	$\dfrac{g_J(\text{Pr})}{g_J(\text{Cs})}$	0.365 ±0.002	0.731 ±0.004	0.727	53 L1	49 M1
Au^{197}	$^2S_{1/2}$	$\dfrac{g_J(\text{Au})}{g_J(\text{Cs})}$	1.00096(57)	2.00420(58)	2.002	53 W1	
Hg[h]	$6s6p\,{}^3P_1$	$\dfrac{g_J(\text{Hg})}{g_p}$	0.74106(270)	1.4838(270)	1.50	52 B1	

(a) Experiment was done on xenon with its natural isotopic abundance.

(b) The atomic state is the ground state electronic configuration unless a different electronic configuration is indicated.

(c) The quantity $g_J/g_J(\text{H})$ is obtained by combining the appropriate measured quantities.

(d) The experimental value of g_J for an atom is obtained by combining the directly measured quantity involving the g_J of the atom with other measured quantities given in the Table in order to obtain g_J/g_l. (The unit is $g_l = 1$.) For all cases, the measured value of g_l/g_p is required, and for several atoms with the best known g_J values the inaccuracy of about 9 ppm for this quantity provides the principal part of the quoted errors.

(e) Errors are indicated by the numbers in parentheses in parts per million (ppm).

(f) This number is the unweighted average of the two experimental values in the references.

(g) The latest value $\alpha^{-1} = 137.0390 \pm 0.0012$ has been used in calculating theoretical g_J values. See reference 57 S1.

(h) Result applies to the naturally occurring odd A isotopes of mercury.

(i) The quantity g_p is the nuclear g-value of the proton in a spherical sample of mineral oils.

REFERENCES TO TABLE 2

28 B1   G. Breit, Relativistic contributions to g_J theory, *Nature* **122**, 649 (1928).

40 M1   H. Margenau, Relativistic contributions to g_J theory, *Phys. Rev.* **57**, 383 (1940).

41 L1   W. E. Lamb, Jr., Internal diamagnetic field in atoms, *Phys. Rev.* **60**, 817 (1941).

47 B1   G. Breit, Electron spin magnetic moment (α) theory, *Phys. Rev.* **72**, 984 (1947).

48 B1   G. Breit, Electron spin magnetic moment, *Phys. Rev.* **74**, 656 (1948).

48 K1   P. Kusch and H. M. Foley, Electron g_s from atomic g_J values experiment, *Phys. Rev.* **74**, 250 (1948).

48 S1   J. Schwinger, Electron spin magnetic moment (α) theory, *Phys. Rev.* **73**, 416 (1948).

49 K1   P. Kusch and H. Taub, g_J alkali atoms experiment, *Phys. Rev.* **75**, 1477 (1949).

49 M1   "Atomic Energy Levels," United States Department of Commerce, N.B.S. Circular 467.

49 N1   E. B. Nelson and J. E. Nafe, g_J(D) experiment, *Phys. Rev.* **76**, 1858 (1949).

49 P1   M. Phillips, Effect of nuclear mass on atomic g_J theory, *Phys. Rev.* **76**, 1803 (1949).

49 S1   J. Schwinger, Electron spin magnetic moment (α) theory, *Phys. Rev.* **76**, 790 (1949).

50 K1   R. Karplus and N. M. Kroll, Electron spin magnetic moment (α^2) theory, *Phys. Rev.* **77**, 536 (1950).

50 M1   A. K. Mann and P. Kusch, g_J (In) experiment, *Phys. Rev.* **77**, 435 (1950).

51 G1   J. H. Gardner, g_L/g_p experiment, *Phys. Rev.* **83**, 996 (1951).

52 B1   J. Brossel and F. Bitter, g_J(Hg) experiment, *Phys. Rev.* **86**, 308 (1952).

52 F1   P. Franken and S. Koenig, g_J(K) experiment, *Phys. Rev.* **88**, 199 (1952).

52 K1   Koenig, Prodell, and Kusch, g_J(H)/g_p experiment, *Phys. Rev.* **88**, 191 (1952).

52 K2   J. G. King and V. Jaccarino, g_J(Cl) experiment, *Phys. Rev.* **87**, 228A (1952).

52 P1   M. Phillips, Effect of configuration mixing on g_J of atoms, *Phys. Rev.* **88**, 202 (1952).

52 R1   E. B. Rawson and R. Beringer, g_J(O) experiment, *Phys. Rev.* **88**, 677 (1952).

52 W1   Weinreich, Tucker, and Hughes, g_J(Ne) experiment, *Phys. Rev.* **87**, 229A (1952).

53 A1   A. Abragam and J. H. Van Vleck, g_J(O) theory, *Phys. Rev.* **92**, 1448 (1953).

53 B1   Brix, Eisinger, Lew, and Wessel, g_J(Cr) experiment, *Phys. Rev.* **92**, 647 (1953).

53 H1   Hughes, Tucker, Rhoderick, and Weinreich, g_J(He) experiment, *Phys. Rev.* **91**, 828 (1953).

53 L1   H. Lew, g_J(Pr) experiment, *Phys. Rev.* **91**, 619 (1953).

53 P1   W. Perl and V. W. Hughes, g_J(He) theory, *Phys. Rev.* **91**, 842 (1953).

53 P2   W. Perl, Relativistic contributions to g_J of multielectron atoms, *Phys. Rev.* **91**, 852 (1953).

53 W1   G. Wessel and H. Lew, g_J(Au), g_J (Ag) experiment, *Phys. Rev.* **92**, 641 (1953).

54 B1   R. Beringer and M. A. Heald, g_J(H)/g_p experiment, *Phys. Rev.* **95**, 1474 (1954).

54 H1   M. A. Heald and R. Beringer, g_J(N) experiment, *Phys. Rev.* **96**, 645 (1954).

54 K1   J. G. King and V. Jaccarino, $g_J(Br)$ experiment, *Phys. Rev.* **94**, 1610 (1954).

54 K2   K. Kambe and J. H. Van Vleck, $g_J(O)$ theory, *Phys. Rev.* **96**, 66 (1954).

54 L1   Louisell, Pidd, and Crane, Free electron g_s/g_L experiment, *Phys. Rev.* **94**, 7 (1954).

55 D1   H. G. Dehmelt, $g_J(P)$ experiment, *Phys. Rev.* **99**, 527 (1955).

55 W1   L. D. White, $g_J(H, 2^2S_{\frac{1}{2}})$ experiment, *Phys. Rev.* **98**, 1194A (1955).

56 F1   P. Franken and S. Liebes, Jr., g_L/g_p experiment, *Phys. Rev.* **104**, 1197 (1956).

57 D1   Drake, Hughes, and Lurio, $g_J(Ne)$, $g_J(A)$ experiment, *Bull. Am. Phys. Soc.* II, **2**, 37 (1957).

57 F1   H. Friedburg and H. Kuiper, $g_J(Xe)$ experiment, *Naturwiss.* **44**, 487 (1957).

57 G1   Geiger, Hughes, and Radford, $g_J(D)$ experiment, *Phys. Rev.* **105**, 183 (1957).

57 P1   A. Petermann, Electron spin magnetic moment $1(\alpha^2)$ theory, *Nuclear Phys.* **3**, 689 (1957).

57 S1   C. M. Sommerfield, Electron spin magnetic moment (α^2) theory, *Phys. Rev.* **107**, 328 (1957); *Ann. Phys.* **5**, 26 (1958).

57 T1   Y. Ting and H. Lew, $g_J(Cu)$ experiment, *Phys. Rev.* **105**, 581 (1957).

58 D1   H. G. Dehmelt, g_s/g_J experiment, *Phys. Rev.* **109**, 381 (1958).

58 D2   Drake, Lurio, Hughes, and White, g_J (He) experiment, *Bull. Am. Phys. Soc.* II, **3**, 7 (1958).

58 I1   F. R. Innes, g_J (O) theory, *Bull. Am. Phys. Soc.* II, **3**, 8 (1958); also F. R. Innes and C. W. Ufford, *Phys. Rev.* **111**, 194 (1958).

58 L1   Lurio, Drake, Hughes, and White, g_J (Ne) and g_J (A) experiment, *Bull. Am. Phys. Soc.* II, **3**, 8 (1958).

58 R1   H. E. Radford and V. W. Hughes, g_J (O) experiment, *Bull. Am. Phys. Soc.* II, **3**, 8 (1958).

58 R2   H. E. Radford, g_J (F) experiment, private communication; also *Bull. Am. Phys. Soc.* II, **3**, 325 (1958).

5

Hyperfine Structure Measurements in the Metastable 2S State of Hydrogenic Atoms*

P. KUSCH

Columbia University, New York, New York

The typical atomic or molecular beams experiment on the spectroscopy of atoms or molecules at electronically generated frequencies differs from all other spectroscopic experiments in that a transition is detected through an observation of the atoms or molecules that have undergone transition rather than on the radiation that has been absorbed or emitted. In the most common atomic beam spectroscopic experiment an atom or molecule has a differential trajectory through an apparatus depending on whether or not the atom has made a transition at some point along its trajectory. The number of atoms that arrive at some specified point is then a measure of the probability of transition in the atoms. The general methods are well known and will not be further discussed here.

It is, however, possible to perform atomic beam spectroscopic experiments on the metastable state of the hydrogen-like atoms that depend on a wholly different principle for the detection of transitions. Detection of transitions may be accomplished because it is possible in principle and feasible in practice to depopulate certain of the component levels in the metastable $2^2S_{\frac{1}{2}}$ state of the hydrogenic atoms. The process of depopulation always leads to a return of the atom to the ground, $1S$, state with the emission of an energetic photon. In fact, the experiments are possible because of the large excess energy of the metastable state which allows the highly selective detection of atoms in this state as well as the detection of the process of depopulation through the photon energy.

It is at once evident that the extremely precise definition of a beam that is necessary in experiments in which a transition is detected through

* The work described in this paper has been supported in part jointly by the Signal Corps, the Office of Naval Research, and the Air Force Office of Scientific Research.

a differential trajectory is not here necessary. This feature of the experiments to be described has considerable value, for it allows the use of a large beam aperture under circumstances in which a high beam intensity is difficult to achieve. In the case of experiments on He^{3+} the space charge density within the beam may be kept low through the use of the large available aperture. The aperture is, of course, limited in this case also by the requirement that all metastables in the beam are in the same magnetic field while undergoing transitions and that all metastables be subjected to the same perturbing rf fields, often of high frequency.

The classic experiments of Lamb,[1] his co-workers and others on the fine structure of the $n = 2$ state of hydrogen and ionized helium have made use of the possibility of depopulating the metastable state of hydrogen-like atoms. These experiments will not be discussed here. Two rather atypical atomic beam experiments, less familiar than those of Lamb will be described. In the first[2] of them the hyperfine structures of hydrogen and deuterium in the $2S$ state were measured. In the second of them the hyperfine structure of the helium 3 ion in the metastable state was measured by Novick and Commins.[3]

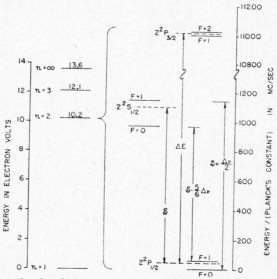

Fig. 1. Energy levels of the hydrogen atom. Lamb Shift $S = 1058$ Mc/sec.
$\Delta E = 10{,}968$ Mc/sec. $\Delta \nu = 178$ Mc/sec.

The energy level system of hydrogen is shown in Fig. 1. The system is essentially the same for ionized helium 3. For He^3 the energy scale on the left is to be increased by a factor of four, so that the $n = 2$ state lies about 40.8 volts above the $n = 1$ state in He⁺. The Lamb shift is 14,042 Mc/sec. The fine structure separation in He⁺ is about 176,000 Mc/sec. The spins of both H¹ and He³ are $\frac{1}{2}$ but since the nuclear magnetic moment of the proton is positive and that of He³ is negative, the hfs is normal in the first case and inverted in the second. The hyperfine structure of the ground state of hydrogen is, of course, accessible to study and the hfs splittings of all three isotopes of hydrogen in the 1S state have been measured[4] with great precision. The hyperfine splitting of the ground state of the He³ ion has not been measured nor has a scheme for making the measurement been proposed that appears to offer a substantial chance of success. The lifetime of the P states is very short (about 1.6×10^{-9} sec for H and less for He⁺) but, in the absence of perturbing fields, that of the 2S state is relatively long, of the order of one-tenth second for H and 2×10^{-3} sec for He⁺. In the experiments that we shall discuss, the velocities of the atoms or ions in the beam are in the range from 4×10^5 to 5×10^6 cm/sec. The distance that a metastable particle may travel without significant decay is thus of the order of many meters, much greater than the length of a beam that is necessary for precise spectroscopic observation.

An electrostatic field mixes the 2P state into the 2S state and the lifetime of the latter is reduced. The application of a moderate electric field for a relatively short time may completely quench the metastable population, that is, return it to the ground state. So effective is the quenching that an electric field is used as a beam flag to determine the total metastable population in a beam. The process of quenching produces new photons but the aperture of the detector presented to these photons is small. This effect of a field also introduces the hazard of accidental quenching of the metastable population by random fields. More importantly, a mixing of the 2S and P states by an electric field gives rise to a shift in the hyperfine structure splitting of the 2S state. For these reasons all experiments have included careful precautions to exclude uncontrolled electrostatic fields, especially in that portion of the trajectory in which line frequencies are determined.

The motional electric field, $E = (v/c) \times H$, serves the same purpose as an electrostatic field and its effect increases with E but also with diminishing separation between a component of the 2S state and one of a P state. Consider the Zeeman splitting of the hyperfine structure of hydrogen in the 2S state shown in Fig. 2. At a field of 575 gauss the level $m_J = \frac{1}{2}$ of the $P_{\frac{1}{2}}$ state crosses the $m_J = \frac{1}{2}$ level (the β levels) of the 2S state. An atom with a velocity of 5×10^5 cm/sec in either one of the β levels has a decay length of about 0.5 mm in a field of 575 gauss perpendicular to the velocity vector while an atom in either one of the levels $m_J = \frac{1}{2}$ (the α levels) has a decay length of about 87 cm. It is apparent that this highly differential behavior may produce a beam of neutral metastable atoms in which the population is entirely in the α levels.

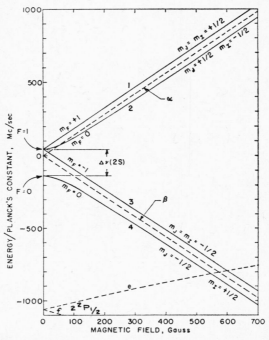

Fig. 2. Zeeman splitting of the hyperfine structure of the 2S state of hydrogen. The dashed lines show the energy level, when hfs is ignored.

The width of a resonance line corresponding to a transition between the component levels of the 2S state is determined entirely by the usual transit time relationship provided that the lifetime of the metastable atom or ion is large compared to the time interval in which the atom is subjected to the radiation field. The width of a resonance line for transitions between a level of the 2S state and one of the P state is determined by the lifetime of the P state and is 100 Mc/sec and 1600 Mc/sec for H and He⁺ respectively.

A transition may be induced between the 2S state and the P state by application of an oscillating electric field of appropriate frequency and amplitude. Atoms or ions that have made the transition to the 2P state decay almost immediately to the 1S state so that this is a mechanism for depopulating but not repopulating the 2S state. For both hydrogen and helium the hyperfine structure separation is, very roughly, the same as the width of the line connecting the $2S$ and P state. The application of a field of a frequency corresponding to the energy difference between one of the hyperfine levels of the $2S$ state and the P state will not, therefore, depopulate only a single one of the hyperfine levels. Nevertheless, it is possible by this mechanism to achieve a significant differential depopulation of the two hfs levels.

With these general statements in mind, we will now discuss the experiments on the hydrogens and on ionized helium 3 in more detail.

Hydrogen

A schematic diagram of the experiment on atomic hydrogen and deuterium is shown in Fig. 3. Molecular hydrogen is thermally dissociated at a temperature of about 2800°K to produce a beam of atomic hydrogen. The dissociation is nearly complete at this temperature. It would be possible to produce atomic hydrogen by use of a conventional Wood's discharge tube as well. The beam traverses a region in which it is bombarded by electrons with an energy of about 13 volts. This serves to excite a fraction of the atoms to the $2S$ state. An approximate calculation of Lamb and Retherford indicates a yield of about one in forty million for the production of the atoms in the $2S$ state under the conditions of the present experiment. Since the momentum of the electron is perpendicular to that of the hydrogen atom there is a recoil dilution, that is, there is a range of recoil angle for any particular velocity and the range itself will depend on the atomic velocity. The subsequent aperture will selectively accept metastable atoms in a

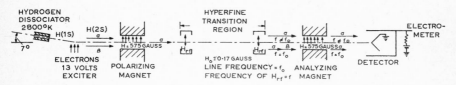

Fig. 3. A schematic diagram of the experimental arrangements used in measuring the hfs of H and D in the $2S$ state.

velocity range more restricted than that of the thermally produced atoms. An adjustment of the angle at which the thermal atoms enter the exciter allows an experimental choice of the velocity range of the metastable atoms.

The atoms in the $2S$ state are now distributed among the several hfs levels. If the atoms traverse a magnetic field of about 575 gauss, those in the β states are very strongly quenched, that is, they return to the ground state with the emission of a photon. The atoms in the α states are only weakly quenched. The atoms that leave the polarizing field are thus predominantly in the α states. In practice the electron bombardment occurs within the polarizing field which then serves the additional purpose of aiding in the collimation of electrons.

The beam now traverses an extended region of space that contains the circuits in which the rf transitions are induced. Those transitions are observable which correspond to a transition from an α state to a β state. By reference to Fig. 2 it is seen that the observable transitions $(F, m; F', m')$ are (1, 1; 0, 0), (1, 0; 1, −1) and (1, 0; 0, 0). The first two of these have a frequency with a linear dependence on field and require for their stimulation an oscillating magnetic field perpendicular to the static field, H_0. The last of these transitions has only a quadratic dependence on field and requires for its stimulation an oscillating field parallel to H_0. By an adjustment of the relative directions of H_{rf} and H_0 both polarizations of H_{rf} occur simultaneously. With H_0 about 0.17 gauss, the frequency of the line (1, 0; 0, 0) exceeds the zero field hfs splitting by about 640 cycles per second. The frequency is thus nearly field independent. A measurement of the frequency of the line (1, 1; 0, 0) allows the determination of the field to a good accuracy. The small correction necessary to derive the zero field hyperfine structure separation from the frequency of the nearly field independent line can then be determined. It should be noted that a line (actually a pair of unresolved lines with a frequency separation of 200 cycles/sec at 0.17 gauss), with only a quadratic dependence of frequency on H_0 may be observed in deuterium and from the frequency of this line the zero field hfs splitting may be deduced after auxiliary lines have been observed to find the magnetic field. Since the hfs splitting in D is considerably smaller than in H, the quadratic term in the line frequency is greater and its determination is subject to greater inherent uncertainties.

Use is made of the method of separated oscillating magnetic fields, first suggested by Ramsey,[5] to induce transitions among the hfs levels. The method has several advantages over other schemes that have been employed but will not be further described here.

After the beam has passed through the transition region it again passes through a field, produced by the analyzing magnet, of about 575 gauss. If no transitions have occurred between the α and β states in the transition region, the flux of metastable atoms through the field is constant. If, however, a transition has occurred, the atoms in the β state are quenched. The flux of metastable atoms is reduced and photons are emitted within the analyzing field. Detection of transitions can be achieved either by a measurement of the flux of metastable atoms that arrive at the detector beyond the analyzing magnet or by a measurement of the photons produced in the magnet. In practice the first of the two methods was used. A metastable atom may eject an electron from a metal surface and the electron current is measured by conventional methods. There is an inevitable flux of photons to the metal surface that also produces an electron current. Since the metastable atoms may be completely quenched by the interposition of an electrostatic field along the beam trajectory, it is possible to make a good determination of the photon background. .

A resonance curve observed for the line in D with only a quadratic dependence on field is shown in Fig. 4. The typical Ramsey pattern is noted, where, however, the auxiliary maxima are not damped as rapidly as in Ramsey's theoretical curve since the velocity distribution of the metastable atoms in which transitions have been observed is considerably sharper than a Maxwellian distribution. The width of the central maximum of a typical resonance curve was 5.5 kc/sec for H and 4.8 kc/sec for D.

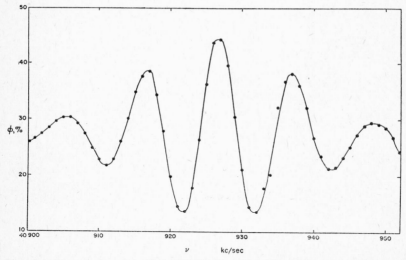

Fig. 4. A resonance curve of the field independent doublet of D in the $2S$ state showing several subsidiary maxima in the Ramsey pattern. The ordinate φ describes the decrease in the flux of metastable atoms.

The experiments yield the following results for the zero field hfs splittings in the $2S$ state of H and D:

$$\Delta\nu\ (2S;\text{H}) = 177\ 556.86 \pm 0.05 \text{ kc/sec, and}$$
$$\Delta\nu\ (2S;\text{D}) = 40\ 924.439 \pm 0.020 \text{ kc/sec.}$$

The ratio of the hyperfine splittings in the $2S$ and the $1S$ states, $R = \Delta\nu\,(2S)/\Delta\nu\,(1S)$, is, to the first order $\tfrac{1}{8}$. A relativistic treatment of the hfs by Breit[6] gives

$$R_{\text{theor}} = (\tfrac{1}{8})[1 + (\tfrac{5}{8})\alpha^2 + 0(\alpha^4)].$$

The present results when combined with previous determinations of $\Delta\nu\,(1S)$ yield:

$$\Delta R = R_{\text{exp}} - R_{\text{theor}} = (\tfrac{1}{8})(13 \pm 3) \times 10^{-7} \text{ for H and}$$

$$(\tfrac{1}{8})(9 \pm 6) \times 10^{-7} \text{ for D.}$$

The existence of a real difference in ΔR for H and D has not been established.

The effects of nuclear structure that give rise to the hyperfine anomaly in the ground state of H and D are not expected to have a differential effect in the $1S$ and $2S$ states and hence to have an effect on R. However, quantum-electrodynamic effects of the order of α^3 may give rise to observable deviations in R. Mittleman[7] has calculated the α^3 corrections to the hfs of the hydrogens. He finds an effect of the same sign as the experimental effect but 1.55 times as great as that observed for hydrogen. The discrepancy is, of course, greater for deuterium. The source of the discrepancy is unknown.

Helium

From the point of view of the information to be derived from the experiment, it would be quite as valuable to study the hfs of He^{3+} in the $1S$ state as in the $2S$ state. The electronic wave functions are known in each case and deviations from hfs intervals calculated on the basis of a simple model would yield information about the structure of the He^3 nucleus. However, it has so far been possible to study the hfs of He^{3+} only in the $2S$ state precisely because it is metastable.

It is possible to conceive of an experiment to study the hyperfine structure of the helium 3 ion in the metastable $2S$ state similar to the one described for the hydrogens. There are, however, several complications that occur because of the charge on the helium ion. The crossing of the $m_J = -\tfrac{1}{2}$ levels of the $2S$ state and the $m_J = \tfrac{1}{2}$ levels of the $2^2P_{\frac{1}{2}}$ state occurs at about 7000 gauss. It is necessary to arrange magnetic fields along the trajectory that will attain this value at two points and a low and constant value over an extended transition region. It appeared to be a formidable task to achieve a configuration of fields with these properties which would allow the ions in a beam of large aperture to follow sufficiently well defined trajectories to yield a useful intensity at the end of the trajectory. A second difficulty arises from the fact that the detection of the metastable atoms by the method used in the case of hydrogen suffers from the defect that ions in the ground state as well as in the metastable state can eject electrons from a metal surface.

A different procedure has, therefore, been adopted.[3] A schematic representation of the experimental arrangements is shown in Fig. 5. The ions, He^{3+}, are produced by electron bombardment in an ion source. The ions in the $1S$ state predominate but there is a useful population in the $2S$ state. They are removed from the source by a low drawout voltage and are then accelerated to the full beam energy which has, in this experiment, been in the range from 5 to 40 ev. Electrostatic focussing lenses are used as shown.

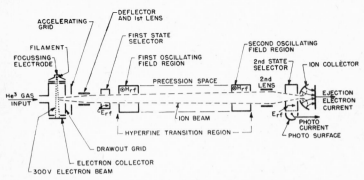

Fig. 5. A schematic diagram of the apparatus used in the measurement of the hfs of He^{3+} in the $2S$ state.

The details of the hfs and Zeeman levels of the $2S$ and $2^2P_{\frac{1}{2}}$ states are shown in Fig. 6. If the lines that connect the $2S$ and the P levels were of small width it would be possible completely to depopulate one of the F levels of the $2S$ state by inducing transitions in the microwave range from the F level to be depopulated to the P state. Since, however, the width of the $^2P_{\frac{1}{2}}$ state is about 1600 Mc/sec and since the hfs splitting is only about 1083 Mc/sec, it is impossible to depopulate completely a single one of the F levels. Nevertheless, by a suitable choice of frequency and power it is possible to achieve a useful excess population in either one of the two F levels. In practice the $F = 1$ level has been depopulated. In the first state selector shown in Fig. 5 the metastable ions are subjected to an electric field with a frequency of 13,350 Mc/sec. As the ions leave the selector there are more than twice as many ions in the $F = 0$ state as in each of the three $F = 1$ substates. When the ions pass through the second state selector there is a further preferential depopulation of the $F = 1$ state. Here, as elsewhere, the preferential depopulation occurs at the expense of a reduction in the flux of metastable ions in the $F = 0$ state as well. Photons are produced in both state selectors; the yield in the first selector is independent of transitions that may occur between hfs levels at a subsequent point in the trajectory.

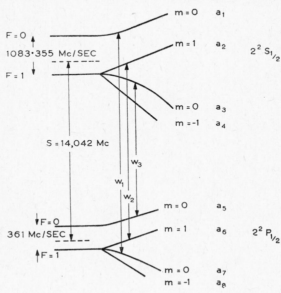

Fig. 6. The Zeeman splitting of the $2^2S_{\frac{1}{2}}$ and $2^2P_{\frac{1}{2}}$ states of He^{3+}. For pictorial purposes the energy intervals are not drawn to scale.

If an oscillating magnetic field of appropriate frequency, amplitude and polarization is applied in the hyperfine transition region or over some portion of it as in the Ramsey method, a transition from the $F = 0$ state to one of the substates of the $F = 1$ state (say the $m = 0$ level) occurs. The population of the $F = 1$, $m = 0$ and $F = 0$, $m = 0$ levels may be almost completely reversed. The complete reversal is possible because the beam is very closely monoenergetic as compared to the case of a beam in which the source of energy of the atoms is thermal where there is a large range of energy of the atoms.

When the beam now enters the second state selector, more transitions to the $2^2P_{\frac{1}{2}}$ state are induced than were induced when no hyperfine transitions occurred. The yield of photons in the selector is thus increased and the flux of metastable ions leaving the selector is decreased. A measurement of either the photon production in the selector or of the flux of metastable ions beyond the selector yields a measure of the transition probability among the hfs levels in the transition region. The photo-detection method was abandoned after initial experiments because of the low signal strength resulting from a poor photo-yield and unfavorable geometry.

The metastable ion detection depends on the differential electron yield when metastable and normal ions impinge on a metal surface. Evidently the differential yield is essential to the detection of transitions since the total ion flux is invariant with respect to the occurrence of transitions among the hfs levels of the 2S state. For the ions in the 1S and 2S states the electron yield per ion is 0.2 and 0.5 respectively. A large electron background occurs because of the great relative abundance of ions in the 1S state. Modulation of the electric field oscillating at 13,350 Mc/sec in the first state selector modulates the metastable component of the beam and hence the electron current. Conventional techniques may then be employed to achieve a high ratio of the signal induced by the rf in the transition region to noise.

It is interesting to note some of the details of the experimental arrangements. The apparatus was designed to avoid several specific hazards principally related to the occurrence of stray electric fields. These might cause an instability in the ion current through the random charging and discharging of layers of organic contaminants on metal surfaces near the beam. They might also cause quenching of metastable ions. Finally, they might serve to mix the 2S and 2P states in the transition region with a consequent shift of the hfs separation from its true value for the 2S state. No organic material was used in the construction of the vacuum envelope and the components contained by it. The envelope was constructed of stainless steel and apertures were sealed with copper or gold gaskets. The system was bakeable and equipped with mercury diffusion pumps. The stability of operation was excellent and a comparison of its operation after it had been baked and its operation when the baking procedure was omitted indicated the value of the procedures which were rather unorthodox in atomic beam practice.

In Fig. 7 is shown the typical Ramsey pattern observed for the transition $F = 0$, $m = 0$, to $F = 1$, $m = 0$. The pattern was observed by use of a photodetector. In Fig. 5 the oscillating fields in the two cavities are shown as out of phase by 180°. The purpose of the phase difference is to reduce the possibility of a Stark shift in the hfs splitting by the oscillating electric field which must accompany the oscillating magnetic field. Because of the phase difference in the two cavities a minimum on the resonance curve is observed at the transition frequency. The auxiliary maxima are very well defined, as compared to the more common case of a beam with a Maxwellian velocity distribution because the beam is very nearly monoenergetic. The resonance curve is shown for two beam energies and the increase of the spacing for the higher energy is precisely as expected.

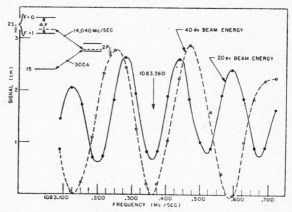

Fig. 7. The observed resonance curve for the transition $F = 0$, $m = 0 \rightarrow F = 1$, $m = 0$ in the $2S$ state of He^{3+}.

A large body of data has been acquired in which the possible effects of a large number of perturbing factors have been investigated. It is found that:

$$\Delta\nu_{\rm exp}(2S, He^{3+}) = 1083.35499 \pm 0.00020 \text{ Mc/sec.}$$

The quantity is of interest for comparison with the value that is theoretically predicted[3] on the basis of the assumption that the He^3 nucleus is a point magnetic dipole. The predicted value is:

$$\Delta\nu_p(2S, He^{3+}) = 1083.557 \pm 0.010 \text{ Mc/sec.}$$

The uncertainty in the predicted value arises principally from the uncertainty in the fine structure constant, α. The discrepancy between the two results is 182 ± 22 parts per million; it exceeds the uncertainty in both experiment and theory within the assumptions of the theory. The discrepancy presumably arises from nuclear structure effects such as those that lead to the hyperfine structure anomaly of hydrogen and deuterium. Nuclear interaction currents and unevaluated higher-order radiative corrections will also contribute to the discrepancy. At the present time no detailed calculation of these effects has been made.

REFERENCES

[1] A general review of the field is given by W. E. Lamb, Jr., *Reports on Progress in Physics*, XIV, 19 (1951), The Physical Society, London.

[2] J. W. Heberle, H. A. Reich, and P. Kusch, *Phys. Rev.* **101**, 612 (1956); H. A. Reich, J. W. Heberle, and P. Kusch, *Phys. Rev.* **104**, 1585 (1956).

[3] R. Novick and E. Commins, *Phys. Rev.* **103**, 1897 (1956). A good many of the details of the experiment are described in the Quarterly Progress Report, Columbia Radiation Laboratory, Columbia University, February 28, 1955 to September 15, 1957. I am indebted to Professor Novick and Dr. Commins for access to unpublished data and for many discussions of the experiment.

[4] P. Kusch, *Phys. Rev.* **100**, 1188 (1955); A. G. Prodell and P. Kusch, *Phys. Rev.* **106**, 87 (1957).

[5] An extended discussion is given in N. F. Ramsey, "Molecular Beams," Section V.4, Oxford University Press, Oxford, 1956.

[6] G. Breit, *Phys. Rev.* **35**, 1447 (1930).

[7] M. H. Mittleman, *Phys. Rev.* **107**, 1170 (1957).

H

6

Shapes of Molecular Beam Resonances

NORMAN F. RAMSEY

Physics Department, Harvard University, Cambridge, Massachusetts

Abstract

A procedure is described for rapid digital computer calculations of the shapes of molecular beam resonances. Resonances are calculated under a wide variety of circumstances. Results are presented which show that variations in the amplitudes of the oscillatory fields change the appearance of the resonance and may even invert it, but the mid-point of the resonance remains at the Bohr frequency. Likewise variations of the fixed field amplitude between oscillatory field regions do not shift the resonance frequency provided the average values of the energy levels equal the uniform values in the oscillatory regions. On the other hand, it is shown that perturbations by neighboring resonances, perturbations by extraneous oscillatory fields, variations of fixed field amplitudes in regions of non-vanishing oscillatory fields, and phase shifts all produce shifts in the resonance frequency whose magnitudes ordinarily depend on the amplitude of the oscillatory field. It is pointed out that there are many ways in which irregularities of the above nature can be achieved accidentally: a change in direction of the oscillatory field, for example, produces an effective phase shift, modulation of the oscillatory field produces extraneous frequencies, etc. General expressions are given for the shift in resonance frequency to be expected with neighboring resonances and with extraneous oscillatory fields.

I. Introduction

Ordinarily in a molecular or atomic beam resonance experiment one measures a resonance curve and then assumes that the mid-point of the resonance is at the Bohr frequency $\nu_0 = (W_q - W_p)/h$. In any precision experiment it is therefore important to know the conditions that can significantly distort the resonance so that the mid-point becomes other than the Bohr frequency.

Unfortunately most of the features of an experiment that distort a resonance also make it difficult or impossible to solve the probability amplitude equations. However, in a recent report, the author[1] has described two procedures for digital computer calculations of the shapes of molecular beam resonances with non-uniform oscillatory fields. One of these applies when only two energy levels and a single oscillatory perturbation is involved. The other involves a much longer calculation but applies with three energy levels and up to nine different perturbations between the energy levels. Unfortunately, the expense of calculations with the latter procedure is sufficiently great that calculations have been made for only a few cases. In the present report a procedure is described which makes possible rapid calculations of problems with three energy levels and several perturbations.

Results of calculations are presented in subsequent sections which show the effects of variations in the oscillatory field amplitudes, perturbations by neighboring resonances, perturbations by oscillatory fields, variations in the fixed field amplitudes, and phase shifts of the oscillatory fields. Various means by which such irregularities can accidentally occur are described.

II. Method of Calculation

Consider a system with three eigenstates, p, q, and r of the Hamiltonian $\mathcal{H}_0$. Let the system be acted upon by the additional time dependent perturbation V and let $\langle p|t \rangle$ represent the transformation function between the eigenvector $|p\rangle$ of the pth eigenstate of $\mathcal{H}_0$ and the general time dependent state vector $|t\rangle$ of the system with $\mathcal{H} = \mathcal{H}_0 + V$. Then,[1]

$$i\hbar \frac{d}{dt}\langle p|t \rangle = \langle p|\mathcal{H}_0|p \rangle \langle p|t \rangle + \langle p|V|p \rangle \langle p|t \rangle +$$
$$+ \langle p|V|q \rangle \langle q|t \rangle + \langle p|V|r \rangle \langle r|t \rangle \qquad (1)_{cyc}$$

together with the two equations obtained by cyclic permutations of p, q, r as indicated by the subscript *cyc* behind the equation number. A wide variety of relevant problems can be included if $\mathcal{H}_0$ and V are restricted to forms which provide Hermitian matrix elements such that

$$\langle p|\mathcal{H}_0|p \rangle/\hbar = a_p$$
$$\langle p|V|p \rangle/\hbar = 0$$
$$\langle p|V|q \rangle/\hbar = b_r \exp i(\omega_{br}t + \delta_{br}) + c_r \exp i(\omega_{cr}t + \delta_{cr}) \qquad (2)_{cyc}$$
$$\langle p|V|r \rangle/\hbar = b_q \exp i(-\omega_{bq}t - \delta_{bq}t) + c_q \exp i(-\omega_{cq}t - \delta_{cq})$$

where a_p, b_p, δ_{bp}, δ_{cp}, etc., are real constants that are not explicit functions of the time, although they may vary along the path of the beam. The quantities ω_{bp}, etc., correspond to the various frequencies of the perturbations and are assumed to be unaltered throughout the transition region.

The advantages of the rapid single perturbation procedure can be achieved with several levels by replacing the actual problem by one which simulates it by a number of iterative steps such that in each step only a single perturbation is present while successive steps may have different perturbations between different energy levels so that the average over several adjacent steps is equivalent to the actual problem being simulated. Then if for a step of duration Δ beginning at time t the perturbation is b_r between levels p and q while all the other perturbations vanish in that step, the probability amplitudes after that step become[1,2]

$$\langle p|t+\Delta\rangle_R = F'_+\langle p|t\rangle_R + G'_+\langle q|t\rangle_R + H'_+\langle p|t\rangle_I + I'_+\langle q|t\rangle_I$$

$$\langle p|t+\Delta\rangle_I = -H'_+\langle p|t\rangle_R - I'_+\langle q|t\rangle_R + F'_+\langle p|t\rangle_I + G'_+\langle q|t\rangle_I$$

$$\langle q|t+\Delta\rangle_R = G'_-\langle p|t\rangle_R + F'_-\langle q|t\rangle_R + H'_-\langle p|t\rangle_I + I'_-\langle q|t\rangle_I \qquad (3)$$

$$\langle q|t+\Delta\rangle_I = -H'_-\langle p|t\rangle_R - I'_-\langle q|t\rangle_R + F'_-\langle p|t\rangle_I + G'_-\langle q|t\rangle_I$$

$$\langle r|t+\Delta\rangle_R = \cos(a_r\Delta)\langle r|t\rangle_R + \sin(a_r\Delta)\langle r|t\rangle_I$$
$$\langle r|t+\Delta\rangle_I = -\sin(a_r\Delta)\langle r|t\rangle_R + \cos(a_r\Delta)\langle r|t\rangle_I$$

where the subscripts R and I indicate real and imaginary components and where

$$F_\pm = \cos\left[(\pm\omega-a_p-a_q)\Delta/2\right]\cos A\Delta/2 +$$
$$\pm(\omega+a_p-a_q)\sin\left[(\pm\omega-a_p-a_q)\Delta/2\right][\sin A\Delta/2]/A$$
$$G_\pm = 2b_r\sin\left[\pm\omega(t+\Delta/2)-(a_p+a_q)\Delta/2\pm\delta\right][\sin A\Delta/2]/A$$
$$H_\pm = -\sin\left[(\pm\omega-a_p-a_q)\Delta/2\right]\cos A\Delta/2 + \qquad (4)$$
$$\pm(\omega+a_p-a_q)\cos\left[(\pm\omega-a_p-a_q)\Delta/2\right][\sin A\Delta/2]/A$$
$$I_\pm = 2b_r\cos\left[\pm\omega(t+\Delta/2)-(a_p+a_q)\Delta/2\pm\delta\right][\sin A\Delta/2]/A$$

with

$$A = [(a_q-a_p-\omega)^2+(2b_r)^2]^{\frac{1}{2}}. \qquad (5)$$

In each successive step only a single perturbation is present so that in each step relations similar to the first four of Eq. (3) give the transformation functions of the two levels affected by the perturbation while the last two equations apply to the unperturbed level.

By successive applications of Eq. (3) the final probability amplitudes can be obtained in terms of the initial amplitudes $\langle p|0\rangle$, etc. This iterative procedure has been programmed for the Harvard Univac I digital computer. In the program the fifteen quantities a_p, b_p, c_p, δ_{bp}, δ_{cp}, etc., may vary along the beam path in an arbitrary fashion provided only that their values can be satisfactorily inferred by linear interpolation between values tabulated at twenty arbitrarily chosen points along the beam. For each resonance frequency the transition probability can be calculated at as many different velocities as desired and these can be averaged with arbitrarily chosen weights to provide an average over any desired probability distribution.

It should be noted that when the above procedure is applied, for example, to the separated oscillatory field method the effective length of the short oscillatory field regions is the sum of the lengths of only those iterative steps in which the particular perturbation of concern occurs in the simulating problem. In any case in which there is reason to doubt the validity of the simulation, a few critical points can be calculated both by the present fast method and the previously described[1] slow but direct method; a comparison of the results indicates the applicability of the simulating problem. In all cases so far for which the same problem has been calculated by both the rapid and the slow method, the agreement has been excellent.

III. Variations in Amplitudes of Oscillatory Perturbations

The above procedure has been used to calculate the effect of unequal amplitudes of the oscillatory fields in the separated oscillatory field resonance method. Fig. 1 shows the resonance to be expected when the first oscillatory field is three times the optimum value while the second is at the optimum value. The shape of the resonance is greatly altered by these oscillatory field amplitudes, in fact, the resonance is converted from a transition maximum to a transition minimum. However, despite this marked change in character, this inequality of oscillatory field amplitudes does not produce a shift in the resonance frequency; the Bohr frequency is still at the point of symmetry of the curve even though it is a minimum instead of a maximum.

Effects obtainable with equal but non-optimum values of the two oscillatory fields have been discussed by the author in earlier articles.[1-4] With excessively weak fields the resonance is weaker but also of a narrower half width.[2] With excessive oscillatory perturbations $2b$ the resonance width is not importantly changed but two extraneous velocity independent resonances are produced at the frequencies $\nu_0 \pm 2bl/(\pi L)$ where l is the length of each of the two oscillatory field regions and L is the distance between them. The effects of gradual application and removal of the oscillatory fields have also been discussed previously.[1]

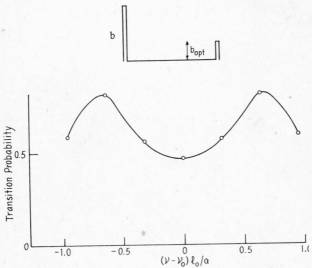

Fig. 1. Resonance shape for separated oscillatory fields with the first oscillatory field three times optimum and the second at optimum value. The amplitude of the perturbation as a function of the distance along the beam is shown in the upper illustration. The transition probability is plotted as a function of frequency in the lower curve.

IV. Variations in Magnitude of the Fixed Field

Variations of the magnitude of the fixed field between (but not in) the oscillatory field regions do not ordinarily distort a molecular beam resonance provided that the average Bohr frequency equals the value of the Bohr frequency in the oscillatory field regions.

However, if the preceding conditions are not attained or if the magnitude of the fixed field varies within the oscillatory field regions, the resonance may be seriously distorted. Fig. 2 shows the distortion when the static field varies in the oscillatory field region. The separated oscillatory field resonance is plotted for two different oscillatory field amplitudes. It is to be noted that the apparent resonance position shifts as a function of the oscillatory field amplitude. The physical reason for this power shift is that the effective field is averaged over slightly different regions with different oscillatory power.

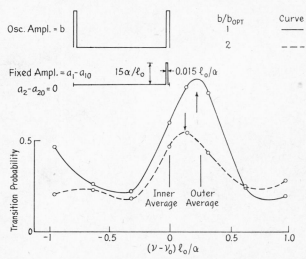

Fig. 2. Distortion of resonance by variation of the fixed field magnitude within the oscillatory field region. The nature of the assumed variation along the length of the beam is shown at the top of the figure and the resonance curve at the bottom. The "inner average" is the average Bohr frequency excluding the oscillatory field region whereas the "outer average" includes this as well.

If the magnitude of the fixed field in a single oscillatory field experiment varies importantly the resonance pattern may be tremendously distorted; one or more extraneous transition maxima can easily be produced in this manner as discussed previously.[2]

V. Distortion by Neighboring Resonances

In systems involving more than two energy levels, the same oscillatory field which produces the desired transition between energy levels p and q may also provide perturbations between level p and another level r, or between s and q. One consequence of this is the production of multiple quantum transitions.[2,5,6] Another consequence, however, is that the presence of this undesired additional perturbation will shift the apparent position of the p–q resonance.

The problem of the simultaneous presence of the three oscillatory perturbations in each of the two oscillatory field regions of the separated oscillatory field method has not been solved in general. However, a theoretical expression can be obtained for the very closely related problem of a molecule which first for a time τ passes through a region where there is the desired perturbation between levels p and q, then for a time T_1 the molecule is in a region of length l_1 in which the p–r and s–q perturbations are excited, then for a time T_2 in a region of length l_2 with no oscillatory perturbations, then for a time T_3 in a region of length l_3 with the p–r and s–q perturbations excited, and finally for a time τ in a region in which only the desired p–q perturbation is excited If $T_1 = T_3 = \tau$ this problem is clearly closely related to the above general problem except that the effects of the extra perturbations are overestimated by a factor of the order of 2 since the extraneous oscillatory perturbations are more effective when they occur between the two p–q transition regions rather than within these two regions.

This problem can be solved in a fashion similar to that of earlier papers[7,8] on the effects of extraneous oscillatory fields provided one assumes for simplicity that the duration τ (but not $b\tau$) of the desired perturbation is small and that the magnitudes b_{pr} and b_{qs} of the undesired perturbations are small compared to the magnitudes of the differences $\omega_{0pr} - \omega_0$ and $\omega_{0sq} - \omega_0$ where ω_0 is the Bohr angular frequency $(W_q - W_p/\hbar$ of the desired transition between levels p and q, while ω_{0pr} is the Bohr angular frequency between levels p and r and ω_{0sq} is between levels s and q. With these assumptions it can be shown that the experimental resonance angular frequency ω_e will be shifted by an amount

$$\delta\omega = \omega_e - \omega_0 = \frac{1}{2}\sum_r{}'' \{\omega_{0pr} - \omega_0\}\{[1 + (2b_{pr})^2/(\omega_{0pr} - \omega_0)^2]^{\frac{1}{2}} - 1\}\beta + \tag{6}$$

$$+ \frac{1}{2}\sum_s{}'' \{\omega_{0sq} - \omega_0\}\{[1 + (2b_{sq})^2/(\omega_{0sq} - \omega_0)^2]^{\frac{1}{2}} - 1\}\beta$$

where

$$\beta = (l_1 + l_3)/(l_1 + l_2 + l_3) \tag{7}$$

and where Σ'' indicates that the summation does not include $r = p$ or q.

If, as in the actual case, all perturbations are simultaneously present for times τ in regions of length l on each side of a perturbation free region of length L, the shift should be similar to the above except that the undesired perturbation will be somewhat less effective. It would appear to be reasonable to assume that Eq. (6) should apply in this case as well with β however being determined approximately by

$$\beta = \tfrac{1}{2}(2l)/L = l/L \tag{8}$$

When

$$| \omega_{0pr} - \omega_o || \gg | 2b_{pr} |,$$

Eq. (6) and (8) become

$$\delta\omega = \tfrac{1}{4}(l/L)\left[\sum_r{}'' (2b_{pr})^2/(\omega_{0pr}-\omega_0) + \sum_s{}'' (2b_{sq})^2/(\omega_{0sq}-\omega_0)\right] \tag{9}$$

The validity of the shifts predicted by Eqs. (6) and (8) has been confirmed by the use of the Univac procedure described in Section II to calculate the shift of the resonance frequency by a neighboring resonance. The Univac calculations can also be extended to conditions for which Eq. (6) is not valid. In the course of these calculations it was found that when the results were averaged over only 5 velocities they varied rather randomly and were very sensitive to the exact velocity distribution. It soon became apparent that this was a genuine effect with a limited discrete velocity distribution and with two or more resonances overlapping within the broad pedestal which characterizes the separated oscillatory field method. This velocity sensitivity arises from the fact that with a single velocity the desired resonance occurs in a region where there are still large sharp subsidiary resonances from the undesired resonance since it is only the velocity distribution which averages these out in the separated oscillatory field method. Furthermore, with large perturbation amplitudes sharp interference effects in the magnitude of the shifts should occur even though they do not occur in Eq. (6) which is based on the assumption $|b_{pr}| \ll |\omega_{0pr} -\omega_0)|$. Since these effects are large, an average over only 5 velocities is inadequate and an average over even 20 velocities provides only moderate accuracy. Similar fluctuations should occur in experiments with severely limited velocity distributions. Novick[9] has reported to the author that he has found such phenomena in his resonance experiments with approximately a single velocity.

The results of the calculations are shown in Fig. 3. In addition to the points calculated by the general Univac program the shifts to be expected by Eqs. (6) and (8) are shown as the full curve. There is general agreement as to the magnitude of the effect, but for the reasons discussed in the preceding paragraph, the accuracy of the calculation is not high since the results were averaged only over twenty discrete velocities.

It should be noted that a perturbation at a given frequency above v_0 produces a shift equal and opposite to that of an equal perturbation the same frequency below v_0. Often neighboring perturbations occur in such mutually compensating pairs. However, before assuming that the compensation is complete, one must confirm that no asymmetry is accidentally produced by slight inequalities of the perturbations or by inequalities in the populations of the molecular states in the beam.

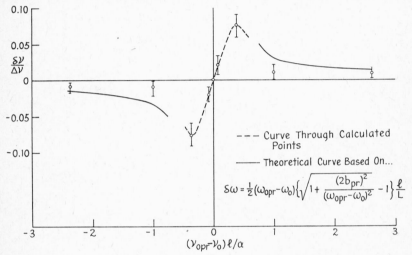

Fig. 3. Shift of resonance frequency by presence of a neighboring resonance. The indicated points are those calculated by the digital computer. The indicated uncertainty arises for the reasons discussed in Section V. The full curve corresponds to Eqs. (6) and (8).

From Eq. (9) it is apparent that if neighboring resonances are a source of major trouble, the shift from this source can be diminished by increasing the length l of the oscillatory field regions; for maximum transition probability $2b_{pr}$ is proportional to $1/l$ so $\delta\omega$ in Eq. (9) is proportional to $1/l$. This can be done up to the limit of the apparatus becoming a single oscillatory field experiment. It should be noted that this increase will accentuate other resonance distortions, such as the one discussed in the preceding section.

VI. Perturbations at Two or More Frequencies

In earlier papers[7,8] the effects of one or more extraneous oscillatory fields have been discussed. However, the earlier discussions were not directly applicable to perturbations in the oscillatory field regions of the separated oscillatory field method since it was assumed that the extraneous oscillatory fields occurred only in the entire intermediate region. However, the theoretical problem is essentially the same as that for neighboring resonances as discussed in the preceding section.

In the separated oscillatory field case, let ω_e be the experimental resonance transition frequency between the two levels p and q. Let the level p be perturbed to the state r at the frequency ω_i by the matrix element

$$_iV_{pr} = \hbar_i b_{pr} e^{i(\omega_i t +_i \varphi_r)} \tag{10a}$$

while q is perturbed by

$$_iV_{sq} = \hbar_i b_{sq} e^{i(\omega_i t + \varphi_s)} \tag{10b}$$

Assume that these perturbations occur only in the two separated oscillatory field regions. Then the discussion of the preceding section may easily be combined with that of the earlier paper to show that the shift in angular frequency is

$$\delta\omega = \omega_e - \omega_0 = \sum_i \{\omega_0 - \omega_i\}\{[1 + (2_i b_{pq})^2/(\omega_0 - \omega_i)^2] - 1\}\beta + \tag{11}$$

$$+ \frac{1}{2}\sum_i \sum_r {}'' \{\omega_{0pr} - \omega_i\}\{[1 + (2_i b_{pr})^2/(\omega_{0pr} - \omega_i)^2] - 1\}\beta +$$

$$+ \frac{1}{2}\sum_i \sum_s {}'' \{\omega_{0sq} - \omega_i\}\{[1 + (2_i b_{sq})^2/(\omega_{0sq} - \omega_i)^2] - 1\}\beta$$

The value of β is given in Eq. (8) and the region of validity of this formula is similar to that discussed for Eq. (6).

It is apparent from a comparison of Eqs. (11) and (6) that the effects of additional oscillatory fields and of additional resonances are closely similar. Thus with two energy levels and a single additional oscillatory field, the resonance will be shifted by just twice the amount shown in Fig. 3. Experimental studies of such shifts have been reported previously.[4]

It should be noted that there are many different ways in which an oscillatory field of a different frequency can occur. As first pointed out by Bloch and Siegert[10] the use of an oscillatory instead of a rotating field produces a perturbation at frequency $-\omega_0$. Alternatively if the fixed field varies its direction in space the result appears as an oscillatory perturbation to the moving molecule. Likewise if the direction of the oscillatory field rotates in space it will appear as a different frequency to the molecule. Furthermore, the basic oscillatory current supplied may easily contain large components at different frequencies. Another important source of extraneous frequencies is that the oscillating field is ordinarily modulated either to detect or to display the resonance. The side band frequencies from the modulation can distort the resonance somewhat; although this distortion is often symmetrical about the resonance frequency it will not be so if one side band is more effective than its symmetrical opposite.

VII. Phase Shifts

Some of the principal sources of asymmetries and frequency shifts in resonance experiments are relative phase shifts of the oscillatory field in different regions. Although the present discussion primarily concerns the separated oscillatory field method, it should be noted that phase shift troubles are ordinarily worse with the single oscillatory field method since there is a much larger region throughout which the phases must be known.

It should be emphasized that there are many different sources of effective phase shifts. The simplest is an erroneous relative phase adjustment of the two oscillatory fields. Theoretical expressions have been published[11] for quantitative calculations of the effect of such simple phase shifts. If any running waves exist in portions of the apparatus through which the beam passes there will be a continuously varying phase shift. Likewise, in a resonant microwave cavity resistive losses can produce phase shifts. Rotation of the direction of the oscillatory field, as in the Millman effect[12] at the ends of the oscillatory fields, produces a phase shift of the rotating component of the field that is effective in producing the transitions.

The effects of both constant and varying phase shifts have been calculated under a wide variety of circumstances. Some of the results are shown in Fig. 4. At the top of the figure is an extreme example with a large amplitude at a different phase. The results show that there is no displacement of the resonance for a phase shift of 0° or 180° but that there is a large shift for a 90° phase shift. The middle of the figure corresponds to a long wavelength running wave. The bottom portion corresponds to smaller amplitudes of running waves. For symmetry of the amplitudes about the center of the apparatus ($\lambda = \mu$ in the figure) the effects cancel. For $\lambda \neq \mu$ a shift occurs which is much less for a short wavelength running wave than a long one. The

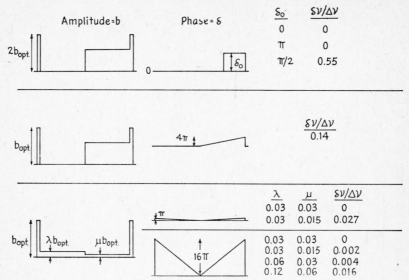

Fig. 4. Effects of phase shifts. The amplitudes of the perturbations and the phase shifts as functions of the distance along the beam are shown in the different cases on the left portion of the figure. The magnitudes of the phase shifts are listed in the tables on the right. $\delta\nu/\Delta\nu$ is the ratio of the shift in resonance frequency to the full half width of the resonance.

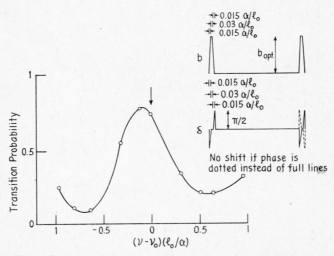

Fig. 5. Effects of phase shifts due to rotation of the direction of oscillatory field at ends of oscillatory field regions. The natures of the assumed amplitudes and phase shifts are indicated schematically at the top of the figure.

condition with $\lambda = 0.03$ and $\mu = 0.015$ for which $\delta\nu/\Delta\nu = 0.002$ is one that might have occurred in the early models of the National Company Atomichron.

In Fig. 5 the shape of the resonance is calculated for a case in which a large rotation of the direction of the oscillatory field occurs on entering and leaving the oscillatory field regions, as in the Millman effect. It can be seen that an appreciable shift occurs. The assumed case is an extreme one; the magnitudes of the frequency shifts are ordinarily much smaller than those assumed.

The author wishes to thank the National Company of Malden, Massachusetts, for supporting this research.

REFERENCES

[1] N. F. Ramsey, *Phys. Rev.* (to be published).
[2] N. F. Ramsey, "Molecular Beams," Oxford University Press, 1955.
[3] N. F. Ramsey, *Phys. Rev.* **78**, 695 (1950).
[4] H. Lewis, A. Pery, W. Quinn and N. F. Ramsey, *Phys. Rev.* **107**, 446 (1957).
[5] P. Kusch, *Phys. Rev.* **93**, 1022 (1954).
[6] H. Salwen, *Phys. Rev.* **99**, 1274 (1955).
[7] N. F. Ramsey, *Phys. Rev.* **100**, 1191 (1955).
[8] J. Winter, *C.R. Acad. Sci., Paris.* **241**, 600 (1955).
[9] R. Novick, Private communication and report at Brookhaven Molecular Beam Conference (1957).
[10] F. Bloch and A. Siegert, *Phys. Rev.* **57**, 522 (1940).
[11] N. F. Ramsey and H. B. Silsbee, *Phys. Rev.* **84**, 506 (1951).
[12] S. Millman, *Phys. Rev.* **55**, 628 (1939).

Comparison of Methods for the Determination of Nuclear Spin as Applied to Radioactive Nuclei

VICTOR W. COHEN

Brookhaven National Laboratory, Upton, Long Island, New York.

Introduction

The role of angular momentum in the theories of atomic nuclei is one of paramount importance. While it was postulated initially by Goudsmit and Back to explain optical hyperfine structure it has assumed the role of a fundamental nuclear property, along with charge and mass, to enter into theories, such as nuclear composition, beta-ray disintegration and parity conservation as well as electromagnetic interactions with atomic electrons. The fact that the spin and related moments, i.e. magnetic dipole, electric quadrupole, and higher moments may enter into interactions of different types, permits us to make inter-related measurements and clear up ambiguities in either theory or the experimental techniques. It was this multiplicity of related phenomena that permitted the early clarification of our understanding of nuclear spin by studies of the alkali atoms in the early 1930's.[1,2,3,4,5] The work on sodium and cesium pointed out that our interpretation of hyperfine structure and the Breit-Rabi interaction were basically correct and that there were errors in the measurements made by optical spectroscopy.

In the study of nuclear spin properties the atomic beam technique has been of extreme importance because of the clear cut nature of its data. When one deals with a monatomic gas at low pressure, interactions involving inter- or intra-molecular forces are completely absent. The other techniques of study of nuclear spin which involve study of gases of greater density, liquids or solids involve forces between the particles which can be evaluated by approximate methods but which cannot be eliminated. It is the purpose of this discussion to compare the various techniques for measurement of spin properties as they apply in particular to radioactive nuclei, to discuss their relative merits and limitations to show how they supplement each other. The various methods considered will be (1) optical spectroscopy, (2) molecular gas microwave spectroscopy, (3) nuclear resonance, (4) paramagnetic resonance and (5) atomic beams. The rf spectroscopy of pure quadrupole transitions is a fruitful technique for study of quadrupole information but there seems little chance of its being of importance to the radioactive nuclei because of the large amount of material required for the investigation.

In this discussion we will not consider those naturally occurring nuclides such as K^{40} and Rb^{87} which possess very weak radioactivity. Techniques applicable to stable nuclei apply equally well to them.

The problems of measurement of spins of unstable nuclei differ from those associated with the corresponding stable ones in three ways: (1) usually only small quantities of material are available, (2) isotopic abundances vary from a few percent to one in 10^7, and (3) the radioactivity of the material under study. This last property makes available a means of detection of the presence of minute amounts of material.

Material Available

The first problem of the radioactive species is that of sample preparation. In general, the amounts of material available are small by standards of the normal techniques. Because of the potential health hazard associated with the radiations from radioactive nuclei it has been necessary in a few cases to provide extensive shielding and remote handling of the apparatus. In most cases, however, the handling problem is simplified by the small amount of material required.

In the past ten years techniques have been developed which make possible the determination of nuclear spin properties using amounts ranging from 10^{10} to 10^{17} atoms.

Processes of production of a particular radioactive nucleus may be by one of two general types, first, such as (n, γ) in which the product is chemically identical with the starting material, and second, such as (n, p) or (d, n) products in which the product has a different atomic number from its parent. The (n, γ) product cannot be separated chemically from its parent except in unusual cases, as for example, a Szilard-Chalmers process. This means that with ordinary neutron capture cross-sections and lifetimes of the order of days or weeks the isotopic purity of the nuclide of interest may be of the order of one part per million. As we shall show later, this definitely rules out the possibility of certain techniques of investigation. In cases in which the capture cross-section for thermal neutrons is large, such as Co^{59} and Eu^{151} a pile irradiation of a year may build up a concentration of the radioactive isotope of well over 1%.

In working with pile produced n, γ products using techniques in which isotopic dilution is not important, one has considerable latitude in choice of amount both of the stable and of the radioactive species. Such a choice may be based upon considerations of convenience.

For the case of isotopes produced by such processes as (n, p) or (d, n), where the product differs chemically from its parent, it can, at least in principle, be separated chemically into a state which is isotopically pure. The great difficulty entering into this problem lies in the fact that the parent material or the reagents used in the separation may contain as trace impurities more of the stable counterpart than of the radioactive product. Normal cyclotron irradiations may produce concentrations less than 1 part per million of the product. It is easy to see how impurities greater than this magnitude might be introduced in the process of chemical separation.

The general subject of the chemistry of preparation of carrier-free nuclides is a difficult one and each one can represent an appreciable part of a research on spin determinations.[6] To prepare a radionuclide with an isotopic purity higher than five per cent may represent a real accomplishment in chemical technique.

Optical Spectroscopy

The field of optical spectroscopy has been widely used to study nuclear spins by hyperfine structure. In all, more than 75 elements have studied over the past thirty years by this method.

A complete analysis of an optical spectrum may yield data on the following nuclear properties:

    (a) Nuclear spin,

    (b) Nuclear-electronic magnetic interaction energy (ΔW),

    (c) Nuclear electric quadrupole interaction energy (if the nuclear spin is greater than $\frac{1}{2}$).

From the fine structure it is possible to compute the mean value of $1/r^3$ for the electronic wave function near the nucleus. This quantity enters into computation of the nuclear electric quadrupole moment from this or other experiments involving nuclear quadrupole interaction.

The multiplicity of an optical electronic energy state will be given by either $2J + 1$ or $2I + 1$, depending upon whether J is less than or greater than I. If the value of I is to be inferred from an observed optical splitting, the levels must be sufficiently well identified to know whether the splitting is due to I or J. There have been several cases where the interpretation of hyperfine structure has lead to uncertain or to incorrect values of I.

The magnitude of the hyperfine structure splitting is a function of the value of the nuclear magnetic moment. The calculation of the moment involves a knowledge of the electronic wave function at the nucleus which, at present, in most cases is not known with sufficient precision to give values comparable to those obtained by nuclear resonance.

In optical hyperfine structure studies one is faced with two problems: (1) obtaining of sufficient light intensity for proper recording, and (2) keeping the spectral lines narrow enough for adequate resolution of closely spaced multiplets. Working with radioactive nuclei one is forced to use minute samples so that the light source must be miniaturized. For efficiency of light utilization the nearest to an ideal source would be one shaped so as to serve as the usual slit of the spectroscope. Sources have been used by several investigators which approach this size and shape.

The phenomena of "cleanup" in a gas discharge tube is a process whereby ions bury themselves in the walls of the tube and are no longer available in the discharge. This of course is very serious if only a minute gas sample is available. In the electrodeless high frequency discharge the ions do not receive enough energy to be removed. Such sources containing about 10^{16} atoms have operated over lifetimes long enough for extensive research without appreciable loss. It should be possible to extend this to even smaller tubes, perhaps less than 0.5 cc, which at a pressure of 0.1 mm would contain only 2×10^{15} atoms.

The hollow-cathode discharge tube cooled with liquid nitrogen or helium has been used extensively for high resolution spectroscopy. It has the advantage of keeping the velocity of the emitting atoms down to an effective temperature near that of the cathode. Such low velocity results in a reduced Doppler broadening. If the voltage across the tube is kept low, the "cleanup" is not great and this type of tube can be miniaturized to an effective volume of one cc or thereabouts.

The choice between the hollow cathode tube and the electrodeless discharge seems to depend upon the preferences of the experimenter as well as the properties of the material under investigation.

In utilizing these types of light sources several investigators have gone to an electronic scanning system which obviates some of the difficulties of photographic methods. A combination of a high resolution grating and a Fabry-Perot interferometer is used. The interferometer spacing is maintained constant in distance but the instrument is in a gas-tight enclosure in which the pressure is changed slowly and continuously. The light intensity at the grating focal plane is received on a liquid nitrogen-cooled photomultiplier and the spectral intensity is recorded graphically.

Optical hyperfine structure investigations are limited to material with an isotopic purity of at least a few per cent. In the light of the discussion in the previous section this is a severe limitation. The method is quite applicable to such nuclides as A^{37} and Kr^{85} which would be very difficult to study by any other means.

Table I includes the spins of those radioactive nuclei that have been determined by optical methods. In a few cases they have also been studied by other techniques. H^3 and C^{14} have been studied by the method of alternating intensities of the rotational bands of the molecular spectrum.

TABLE 1

SPINS OF RADIOACTIVE NUCLEI MEASURED BY OPTICAL SPECTROSCOPY,
NOVEMBER 1, 1957

Element Mass No.	Spin	References
H^3	1/2	Dieke and Tomkins, *Phys. Rev.* **76**, 283 (1949)
C^{14}	0	Jenkins, *Phys. Rev.* **74**, 355 (1955)
Kr^{85}	9/2	Rasmussen, Middleboe, *Z. Physik*, **141**, 160 (1955)
Tc^{99}	9/2	Kessler and Meggers, *Phys. Rev.* **82**, 341 (1951)
Po^{209}	1/2	Vander Sluis and McNally, *J. Opt. Soc. Am.* **45**, 1087 (1955)
Ac^{227}	3/2	Fred, Tomkins, and Meggers, *Phys. Rev.* **98**, 1514 (1955)
Pa^{231}	3/2	Schüler and H. Gollnow, *Naturwiss.* **22**, 511 (1934)
U^{233}	5/2	Vander Sluis and McNally, *J. Opt. Soc. Am.* **44**, 87 (1954)
U^{235}	7/2	Vander Sluis and McNally, *J. Opt. Soc. Am.* **45**, 65 (1955)
Np^{237}	1/2	F. S. Tomkins, *Phys. Rev.* **73**, 1214 (1948)
Np^{239}	1/2	Conway and McLaughlin, *Phys. Rev.* **96**, 541 (1954).
Pu^{239}	1/2	Vanden Berg, Klinkenberg, *Physica* **20**, 461 (1954)
Am^{241}	5/2	Fred and Tomkins, *Phys. Rev.* **89**, 318 (1953)
Am^{243}	5/2	Conway and McLaughlin, *Phys. Rev.* **94**, 498 (1954)

Gas Microwave Spectroscopy

Microwave spectroscopy has been applied to a study of the pure rotational spectrum of gas molecules in the ground electronic state and generally in the lowest vibrational state. The rotational frequencies of many molecules are such that transitions can be observed in the frequency range between a few thousand and a hundred thousand megacycles. These transitions may be split by an interaction between the nuclear electric quadrupole moment and the electric field gradient at the nucleus. From the multiplicity of the resulting spectrum, the relative spacing and the rough relative intensities, one can infer the nuclear spin.[7] Fig. 1 indicates the theoretical pattern to be expected for a typical linear molecule undergoing a $J = 1 \leftrightarrow 2$ transition for different assumed values of the spin.

The scale factor of the separation of the components is proportional to $(e\,q\,Q)$ the interaction between the nuclear electric quadrupole

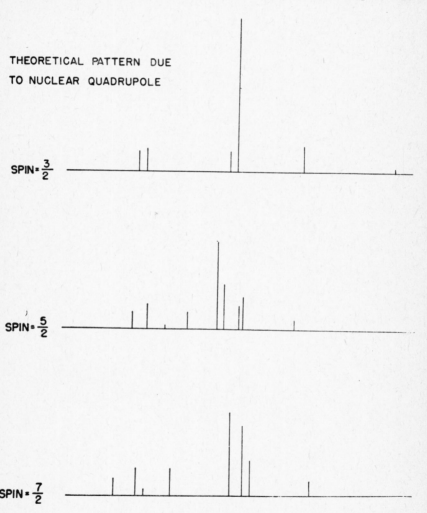

THEORETICAL PATTERN DUE
TO NUCLEAR QUADRUPOLE

SPIN$= \frac{3}{2}$

SPIN$= \frac{5}{2}$

SPIN$= \frac{7}{2}$

Fig. 1. Theoretical microwave rotational spectrum for a linear molecule such as OCS undergoing a transition $J_{1 \leftrightarrow 2}$ for different assumed values of the spin of one of the nuclei.

moment Q and the gradient of the electric field, q. Fig. 2 is an experimental curve obtained with OCS^{35} indicating good agreement with the theoretical pattern for $I = \frac{3}{2}$.[8]

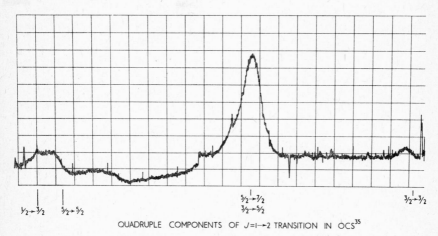

QUADRUPLE COMPONENTS OF $J=I \rightarrow 2$ TRANSITION IN OCS^{35}

Fig. 2. Experimental curve of the spectrum of the $J_{1 \leftrightarrow 2}$ line for OCS^{35}. The relative positions of the components calculated for an assumed spin of $\frac{3}{2}$ are shown below.

Unfortunately the value of q cannot in general be computed with precision, so that no accurate value of Q can be obtained. It is possible, however, to compute a rough approximation of q on the basis of atomic wave functions and the type of chemical bonds involved. The errors in this type of calculation, together with uncertainties concerning the polarization of the inner electron shells, may result in an overall uncertainty as high as 50%.

In the case of two isotopes of the same element, the electronic states are practically identical so that the ratio of the respective electric quadrupole moments will be proportional to their interaction constants. This gives us at least some precise information on electric quadrupole moments.

There are a number of very basic limitations on the applicability of this method:

(a) The element in question must be incorporated into a molecule which has:

(1) a permanent electric dipole moment.

(2) a simple structure such as linear, symmetric top, (in some cases a simple asymmetric rotor is analyzable).

(3) It must be vaporizable to a pressure of at least a few microns, at a temperature attainable in a wave guide system.

(4) The moment of inertia must be such that the rotational states involve low quantum numbers.

(b) The isotopic purity must be not less than about 1 part per 1000.

(c) The total number of atoms required for any spin determination is of the order of 10^{14} to 10^{15}, the limitation depending to some extent on the character of the spectrum.

The limitation on isotopic purity is very severe in that it may prevent the utilization of all the available material. One is limited in the total gas pressure which can be admitted into the spectroscope. An excess will produce pressure broadening of the line. The situation may arise in which only a small fraction of the material available can be utilized.

The Zeeman effect of a microwave line may be studied by placing the wave guide in a magnetic field. Such an experiment may yield information about the nuclear and molecular magnetic moments. Since this type of experiment involves the splitting of one of the components of the normal spectrum, the resulting intensity will be considerably reduced. This means that the isotopic purity required for the Zeeman effect will be higher than that required for a spin determination.

Table 2 contains data on spins and magnetic moments of radioactive nuclei as obtained by microwave spectroscopy.

TABLE 2

SPINS AND MOMENTS OF RADIOACTIVE NUCLEI MICROWAVE SPECTROSCOPY
NOVEMBER 1, 1957

Nucleus	Spin	μ	References
C^{14}	0		A. Roberts, *Phys. Rev.* **73**, 1405 (1948)
S^{35}	3/2	1.00 ± 0.04	Cohen et al., *Phys. Rev.* **76**, 703 (1949); Burke et al., *Phys. Rev.* **93**, 193 (1954)
Cl^{36}	2	1.32 ± 0.08	Townes and Aamodt, *Phys. Rev.* **76**, 691 (1949); Aamodt and Fletcher, *Phys. Rev.* **98**, 1317 (1955)
Se^{79}	7/2	-1.015 ± 0.015	Hardy et al., *Phys. Rev.* **85**, 494 (1952); Hardy et al., *Phys. Rev.* **92**, 1532 (1953)
I^{125}	5/2		Fletcher and Amble, *Bull. Am. Phys. Soc.* **2**, 30 (1957)
I^{129}	7/2		Livingston et al., *Phys. Rev.* **76**, 149 (1949)
I^{131}	7/2		Livingston et al., *Phys. Rev.* **92**, 1271 (1953)

Nuclear Magnetic Resonance

Nuclear magnetic resonance is an extremely accurate method of measuring ratios of magnetic moments. Unfortunately the quantity of material required, considerably greater than that required by other methods, is of the order of 10^{18} to 10^{20} atoms, depending upon the value of the magnetic moment. Isotopic purity of the order of 1/10 to 1% is required. A few measurements have been made on radioactive nuclei of long half-life which for non-scientific reasons are available in gram quantities.

The interaction between a nucleus and an external magnetic field may be complicated by the existence of an electric quadrupole interaction between the nucleus and a non-cubic electric field due to molecular or crystalline environment. If this interaction is small it may result merely in a broadening of the line. If the interaction is large compared to the magnetic spin-lattice interaction, the line may be so broadened as to be undetectable. Some care must therefore be exercised in a choice of compound of the nuclide under study.

In view of the above difficulties and the developments on other techniques it is doubtful whether much work will be done in this field. The results obtained to date by nuclear resonance are shown in Table 3. The fourth column indicates roughly the number of atoms required for the measurement.

TABLE 3

Nucleus	μ		No. of atoms used	Ref.
H^3	2.97876	± 0.00003	10^{22}	(a)
Cl^{36}	1.2838	0.0003		(b)
Tc^{99}	5.65724	0.00040	2×10^{19}	(c)
I^{129}	2.60304	0.0003	2×10^{19}	(d)

(a) Bloch, Graves, Packard, and Spence, *Phys. Rev.* **71,** 55 (1947).
(b) Sogo and Jeffries, *Phys. Rev.* **98,** 1316 (1955).
(c) Walchli, Livingston, and Martin, *Phys. Rev.* **85,** 479 (1955).
(d) Walchli, Livingston, and Hebert, *Phys. Rev.* **82,** 97 (1951.)

Paramagnetic Resonance

The phenomenon of paramagnetic resonance furnishes a means for studying the Zeeman levels of a paramagnetic system. This system can be ionic, atomic, or molecular. It may be in a gas, crystal, or solution. The requirement that a system be paramagnetic is that it have one or more electrons which are magnetically unpaired. As examples of such systems we may cite free atoms in non-singlet states, ions of the iron or rare earth groups, and molecules known as free radicals which are electrically neutral. The method has been used to obtain information about the ground state of ions and the nature of the crystalline fields. However, the electron may interact with a nuclear magnetic moment and thus give us information about which we are here concerned.

There have been several excellent review articles about the inter-actions of ions in crystals.[9,10] We shall present here only a brief discussion of the principles.

In considering the Zeeman effect of paramagnetic ions it is possible to approximate the ion as a free electron, the orbital contribution being, in some respects, "quenched" by the crystalline field. The splitting factor, g, is therefore very nearly 2.

Let us enumerate the most important interactions to which the un-paired electron is subjected in a crystal.

(a) If the crystalline symmetry is non-cubic there will be a Stark splitting of the ground state of the ion in the absence of a magnetic field.

(b) Magnetic dipole-dipole interaction between adjacent para-magnetic ions.

(c) Magnetic interaction between the electron and an externally applied magnetic field.

(d) Magnetic interaction, similar to optical hfs, between the electron and the magnetic moment of the nucleus upon which the electron is bound. This will clearly give a multiplicity to the energy levels of $2I + 1$ which gives us our means of determining I.

(e) Interaction between the nuclear magnetic moment and the ex-ternal applied magnetic field.

The magnetic dipole-dipole interaction (b) is of the order of μ_0/r^3 where μ_0 is the magnetic moment of the electron and r the interionic distance. By placing the ion in a diamagnetic lattice with a dilution of 1/100 to 1/1000 this interaction may be reduced below a significant value. Term (e) above is very small in all magnetic fields generally used, 3–10 kg. Fig. 3 illustrates the three remaining terms (a), (c) and (d), for a typical case of V^{++} diluted in a Zn Tutton salt[11]. The zero field splitting is due to the Stark effect. In a weak field the splitting due to the magnetic field is, to a first approximation, the Zeeman effect. In the strong field or Paschen-Back region the nuclear interaction results in a multiplicity of $2I + 1$. The scale factor of the strong field splitting is determined by the ΔW term or the hfs interaction energy.

In a paramagnetic resonance experiment the specimen is placed in a resonant cavity in the region where the microwave magnetic field is a maximum and perpendicular to the externally applied magnetic field. The radiation frequency is maintained constant and equal to the natural frequency of the cavity. The external magnetic field is varied slowly

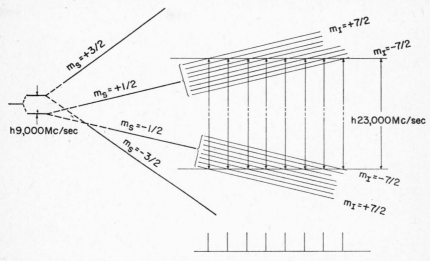

Fig. 3. Schematic Zeeman energy level diagram of the V^{++} ion in a Tutton salt. The spectrum for the hyperfine components of the $m_s(\frac{1}{2} \longleftrightarrow -\frac{1}{2})$ transition is shown below.

and as the energy difference between the two levels for which a transition is allowed satisfies the condition.

$$|E_2 - E_1| = h\nu$$

one observes an absorption of microwave energy.

A typical spectrum for a mixture of two stable isotopes with different spins, V^{50} ($I = 6$, 20% of total V) and V^{51} ($I = \frac{7}{2}$, 80%) is shown in Fig. 4.[11] The magnetic moments as well as the spins are different, giving rise to a complex spectrum. Where certain lines overlap, obviously the weaker one cannot be resolved. If the abundance of the weaker one had been very much less, clearly the lines would have been lost in the tails of the stronger lines. The lowest practical isotopic concentration for a spin determination is in the vicinity of 1%.

Here, as in optical hyperfine structure, the splitting is a function of $\Delta\nu$ and the nuclear magnetic moment cannot be evaluated directly from the experiment. If one can observe a resonance spectrum for two isotopes the ratio of the two $\Delta\nu$'s can be related to the ratio of magnetic moments to within an accuracy at best of about 1 part in 1000.

The efficiency of utilization of a rare isotope is severely limited if one is using a single crystal. On growing a single crystal from solution one must necessarily leave a major fraction of the solute still in solution.

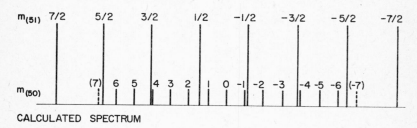

CALCULATED SPECTRUM

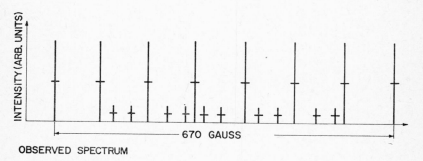

OBSERVED SPECTRUM

Fig. 4. Theoretical and observed spectrum of V^{++} ion with V^{50} and V^{51} present in a ratio of about 1 to 4.

One may avoid some of the problems of working with single crystals by going to solutions. Several elements have exhibited hyperfine structure in paramagnetic resonance spectra in dilute solutions of organic complexes. This is true for B, V, N, C, and Be.[12] Aqueous solutions of inorganic ions can be studied in the region of 9,000 Mc. At 25,000 Mc water has a very high dielectric absorption so that it cannot be used in this region of frequency. Phosphorus, arsenic and antimony dissolved in solid silicon in a concentration of about 10^{-4} and at temperatures of a few degrees absolute, are in the atomic state and show paramagnetic resonance. Hyperfine structure patterns of these elements can thus be studied.[13]

It is difficult to specify the lower limit of material necessary for a spin determination. The sensitivity will depend in part upon the number of states into which the ground state is split. This may be quite appreciable for the case of V^{50}, for example, with a nuclear spin of 6 giving rise to 13 hfs components for each electronic state, which in this case of the

Tutton salt is 3 for each of two equivalent ions, giving rise to a total of 78 states. The Boltzmann factor relating population of the two m_j states shows that by going to low temperatures an appreciable gain in sensitivity is available. Such a gain is quite possible for crystals but will not be available for liquid solutions. Solutions, on the other hand, enable one to utilize all of the material which may be available. In practice results have been obtained with crystals using samples of 10^{15} atoms and in favourable cases one may hope to do better.

Feher[14] has developed a modification of paramagnetic resonance in which the electron resonance line is enhanced by a simultaneous application of a radio frequency field corresponding to the energy interval of the hyperfine splitting. This double resonance applied near 1°K makes possible a determination not only of the spin and $\Delta\nu$ but also g_I. By use of this method he has measured both the spin and moment of P^{32} using a sample of 4×10^{14} atoms in a solid solution in Si^{15}. This technique, while more complex than simple paramagnetic resonance, should prove a valuable tool because of its extra sensitivity and the prospect of obtaining additional information.

A further variation of paramagnetic resonance available for radioactive nuclei with spins of 1 or greater has been developed by Jeffries[16] and by Pipkin and Culvahouse.[17] At low temperature, a partial nuclear polarization can be induced by the application of a microwave field. This polarization is detected by the anistropy in the emitted γ radiations. This has the very valuable property of being independent of the presence of the stable isotope of the element under investigation. It has been successfully applied to Mn^{52}, $Co^{60(16)}$, and As^{76}.[17]

The spin data of radioactive nuclei which have been measured by paramagnetic resonance methods are listed in Table 4.

Atomic Beams

For the past 25 years the atomic beam technique has been a powerful tool for determining the spin properties of nuclei. Because of the simplicity of the ground state of the atoms studied and the absence of environmental interactions the results have been clearly interpreted. As each advance in beam detection was developed a new group of elements was attacked. After the initial detection by the deposit of a visible film, the surface ionization detector opened up extensive work on the alkalis. The mass spectrometer, especially when combined with an electron ionizer, opened up research to a wide variety of elements such as B, Sb, Au, Ag, and Pr with, undoubtedly, many more to follow. The use of the radiations from radioactive nuclei furnishes a powerful means of detection. Since its first application by Smith and Bellamy in

TABLE 4

SPINS AND MOMENTS OF RADIOACTIVE NUCLEI BY PARAMAGNETIC RESONANCE

OCTOBER 1, 1958

Nucleus	Spin	μ	References
P^{32}	1	0.2523 (3)	Feher et al., Phys. Rev. **107**, 1463 (1957)
Mn^{53}	7/2	5.050 (7)	Dobrowolsky, Phys. Rev. **104**, 1378 (1956)
Co^{56}	4	3.855 (7)	Jones et al., Phys. Rev. **102**, 738 (1956)
Co^{57}	7/2	4.6 (2)	Baker et al., Proc. Phys. Soc. A **66**, 305 (1953)
Co^{58}	2	4.052 (11)	Dobrov and Jeffries, Phys. Rev. **108**, 60 (1957)
Co^{60}	5	3.800 (7)	Dobrowolsky et al., Phys. Rev. **101**, 1001 (1956)
As^{76}	2	−0.906 (4)	Pipkin and Culvahouse, Phys. Rev. **106**, 1102 (1957)
Ce^{141}	7/2	0.89 (9)	Kedzie et al., Phys. Rev. **108**, 54 (1957)
Nd^{147}	5/2	0.56	Kedzie et al., Phys. Rev. **108**, 54 (1957)
Eu^{152}	3	2.0	Abraham et al., Phys. Rev. **108**, 58 (1957)
Eu^{154}	3	2.1	Abraham et al., Phys. Rev. **108**, 58 (1957)
U^{233}	5/2	0.5	Dorain et al., Phys. Rev. **105**, 1307 (1957)
U^{235}	7/2	0.3	Hutchinson et al., Phys. Rev. **102**, 292 (1956)
Np^{237}	5/2	6.0	Bleaney et al., Phys Mag. **45**, 992 (1954)
Pu^{239}	1/2	0.4	Bleaney et al., Phil. Mag. **45**, 773, 991 (1954)
Pu^{241}	5/2		Bleaney et al., Phil. Mag. **45**, 991 (1954)

Note: Probable errors are given in parentheses and the figures refer to the last significant figure of the value of μ. Where no probable error is given it may range from 25 to 50%.

1951[19] it has been applied to a very wide range of nuclei and has given new impetus to the field of measurement of nuclear spins.

At the time of this writing there are least nine laboratories throughout the world equipped to study atomic beams by this method.[20] The detection technique consists simply of allowing the beam to strike a solid surface upon which the atoms will stick. After a standard deposition time, the target is removed and its radioactivity is measured, giving an index of the beam intensity averaged over the time of deposit. One deposition is made for each condition of applied rf or magnetic field. This constitutes a slow procedure compared to the continuously reading detector, but it is very effective.

The schematic features of most of the experiments may be described by reference to the Breit-Rabi equation[21] for the hyperfine energy of an atom in a $^2S_{\frac{1}{2}}$ state with nuclear spin I,

$$W_I(\pm\tfrac{1}{2}m) = -\frac{\Delta W}{2(2I+1)} + g_I\mu_0 Hm \pm \frac{\Delta W}{2}\left(1 + \frac{4m}{2I+1}x + x^2\right)^{\frac{1}{2}}$$

where the $+$ of the $\pm$ sign refers to the state for $F = I + \frac{1}{2}$ and the $-$ refers to $I - \frac{1}{2}$, and the field parameter

$$x = \frac{(g_J - g_I)\mu_0 H}{\Delta W}$$

Figure 5 illustrates graphically the behavior of W as a function of

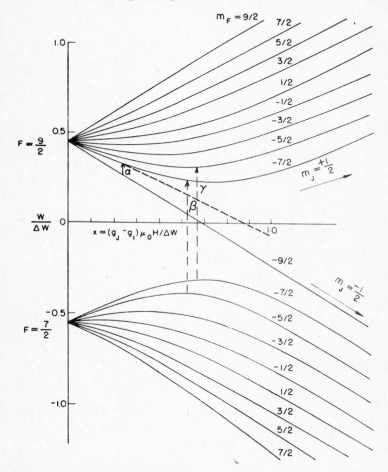

Fig. 5. Zeeman energy levels for an atom in a $^2S_{\frac{1}{2}}$ state with a nuclear spin of 4 as calculated by the Breit-Rabi formula.

x for an arbitrarily chosen value for I of 4. In the strong field the states are characterized by two groups, $m_j = +\frac{1}{2}$ and $m_j - \frac{1}{2}$. In a non-uniform magnetic field those atoms in the $+\frac{1}{2}$ state will be deflected toward the weak field while those in the $-\frac{1}{2}$ state will be deflected in the opposite direction.

The general schematic arrangement of the apparatus is shown in Fig. 6. We see here an oven, non-uniform magnetic fields A and B, a uniform magnetic field region C on which the oscillatory magnetic field

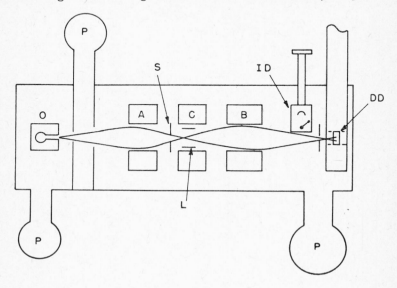

SCHEMATIC OF APPARATUS

Fig. 6. A typical schematic arrangement of a magnetic resonance flop-in type of apparatus: O—oven, P—pumps, S—defining slit; A, B, C refer to the A, B, and C fields; L—Oscillatory field loop; ID—the surface ionization detector for monitoring the beam with a stable isotope; DD—deposition detector for radio-active atoms.

can be superimposed, and the slit which defines that portion of the beam which strikes the detecting target. In the A field region the atoms in the two m_I states will be deflected in opposite directions. The gradients of both the A and B fields are oriented perpendicular to the beam axis and in the same direction. For either state the deflection produced by the B field will be in the same direction as that produced by the A field as long as the atoms pass adiabatically over the entire trajectory. If now in the C region they make any transition from one group to the other the sign of the deflection will change and they will be focused to the detecting slit and strike the target.

The transition α in Fig. 5 will satisfy the condition for an atom to be "flopped", i.e. to undergo a transition in which m changes by ± 1. In this type of experiment the detector receives no beam material unless the oscillatory field is in resonance with the energy of a transition.

The transition α in Fig. 5 has the convenient property that in the weak field region, i.e. where the energy states for the various m values are approximately linear in H, the transition frequency ν at a given H is a function only of I, not of $\Delta\nu (= \Delta W/h)$

$$\nu = \frac{2\mu_0 H}{h(2I+1)}.$$

In measuring the spin of a particular nucleus one knows initially whether its spin will be integral or half-integral according to whether the mass number is even or odd. One may then compute the values of the transition frequency for all possible assumed values of I and a known H. Each of these frequencies is applied in turn and one of them must satisfy the flop-in condition. In principle, then, only a few observations should be necessary to establish the value of the spin.

Once I is determined, the next quantity of interest is $\Delta\nu$, the hfs interaction constant. This constant is, in effect, the scale factor of the abscissa in Fig. 5 and can be evaluated with fair precision by determining the curvature of the energy level diagram in the intermediate field region. Once the frequency is determined at a known field in the linear region as described above, one increases the field by a small amount and then searches for a resonance at a frequency slightly higher than that value extrapolated from the weak field data. From this departure from a linear extrapolation one may make a very rough estimate of $\Delta\nu$. Using this value of $\Delta\nu$ one uses the Breit-Rabi formula to calculate the frequency expected for a slightly higher value of the field. The neighborhood of this value is searched and from the observed resonance frequency a more precise value of $\Delta\nu$ may be computed. This procedure is repeated successively at higher fields until the desired accuracy is obtained. If $\Delta\nu$ can be evaluated to better than one megacycle the zero field transition can be looked for and the optimum precision for $\Delta\nu$ can be obtained. Precision of the order of 1 part in 10^5 is not at all difficult.

Where precision measurements of both $\Delta\nu$ and g_I have been made it has been found that the Fermi-Segrè[22] formula, which relates ΔW, I and g_I

$$\Delta W = \tfrac{16}{3}\pi g_I(2I+1)\psi(0)^2$$

K

is not quite accurate. This formula treats the nuclear-electronic magnetic interaction as though the nucleus acted as a point dipole. For a more precise treatment, considering the penetration of the electron inside the nuclear volume, one must consider the nuclear magnetization to result from a combination of nucleon intrinsic magnetic moments and orbital contributions. Over the nuclear volume, therefore the interactions in two isotopes of the same element will differ.

The departure from the Fermi-Segrè formula has been expressed for the ratio of two ΔW's for two isotopes by defining a correction, Δ, known as the hfs anomaly, by the equation

$$\frac{\Delta W_1}{\Delta W_2} = \frac{g_I^{(1)}}{g_I^{(2)}} \frac{(2I_{(1)}+1)}{(2I_{(2)}+1)} \left(1 + \Delta\right)$$

The significance of the hfs anomaly in nuclear theory has been discussed by Bohr and Weisskopf.[23] One might expect that as different models of nuclear composition are proposed this data may be of value in support or contradiction with theory.

The hfs anomaly has been evaluated for several sets of isotopes where the g_I could be determined with sufficient accuracy. The values of Δ for various combinations has ranged from about 1×10^{-4} to 3×10^{-3}.

In view of the small values of Δ, g_I must be determined with high precision. With materials available in macroscopic quantities this is quite simple by nuclear resonance methods. To determine g_I from atomic beam experiments requires an experiment of a high order of precision.

If one examines, for example, the two transitions labelled β, γ in Fig. 5, they will be approximately equal but will differ by a small term $\delta\nu = (g_I \mu_0 H/h)$. The two components of this apparent doublet must be resolved and the separation measured with precision of 1 part in 10^3 or better in order that Δ may be evaluated.

In a typical example, this splitting may be of the order of 200 kc as compared to a mean frequency of a few thousand megacycles. In order to measure Δ, therefore, one must measure the resonance frequencies to a precision of at least 1 part in 10^7. There are other possible transitions which may be used to determine g_I but they all require very sharp and precisely determined resonances. Measurements of this kind have been made for Cs^{134}, Cs^{135} and Cs^{137} by Stroke[24] using the surface ionization detector and mass spectrometer. It appears quite feasible to measure Δ by radioactive detection and, in fact, the problem is being actively pursued in at least two laboratories.

A significant step in the development of the technique of radioactive detection was made by the group at the University of California at Berkeley by taking advantage of the fact that the area of beam deposition on the target is extremely small. The radioactivity of the target is detected with a scintillation crystal whose area is merely large enough to cover the deposit. Such a small crystal produces a small background due to natural contamination so that significant data can be obtained with very small amounts of material.

The problem of radioactive detection requires that the beam material should have a high probability of sticking to the target surface on the first impact. The sticking properties of gas atoms on solid surfaces are not well understood, partly because most surfaces in an atomic beam apparatus are, strictly speaking, not "pure". The effects of adsorbed films from the atmosphere or from various vapors present inside the vacuum system result in a surface which may not be accurately reproducible or may not be the same as that of another investigator using the same nominal materials. A few surfaces have been found which empirically seem to work with high efficiency. These are lampblack, sulfur, copper cooled with liquid nitrogen, and, with slightly lower efficiency, tungsten. Among the elements which have been detected by this means, are: Na, K, Cs, Cu, Ag, Au, In, Tl, Al, Sn, I, Bi, Am.

In detecting by radioactive deposition the presence of the stable isotope is not a drawback. In fact, an excess of stable over unstable atoms may be advantageous from the standpoint of being easier to manipulate. Problems such as adsorption on the oven walls are vastly reduced if the oven load is macroscopic rather than microscopic. Chemical preparation of products obtained by reactions such as cyclotron (d,n) or pile (n,p) are greatly facilitated by addition of large amount of inert carrier.

An interesting variation of the atomic beam geometry which permits greater collective efficiency was developed independently by Paul at the University of Bonn[25] and by Hamilton at Princeton.[26] This consists of using for A and B fields a multipolar system shown in Fig. 7. Such a field has the property that the gradient is everywhere directed toward the beam axis in spite of the fact that the value of the field itself varies in a complex manner. Geometrically the effect of such a field on a beam which originates from a point-source oven is similar to that of a thin lens operating on rays of light. The schematic arrangement of the beam system is shown in Fig. 8. Atoms in one m_j group of magnetic states will see the A field as a converging lens, while those in the opposite m_j group will see it as diverging. After passing through the C field region the B field acts in a similar manner to the A. One cannot change the orientation of the field gradient. An atom can impinge on the ring collector only if it undergoes a transition induced by the oscillatory field in the C field region so that its trajectory avoids the beam stops as indicated.   This technique effectively focuses in two dimensions while the conventional A and B fields focus only in one dimension. The

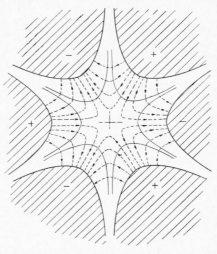

Fig. 7. Cross-section of the 6-pole deflecting magnets used by Hamilton and co-workers. The field gradient is directed toward the axis and is proportional to the distance from the axis.

result is that the solid angle of trajectories which leave the oven and can be received by the detector is very much higher than in the conventional system. One can therefore use a smaller charge of active material in the oven.

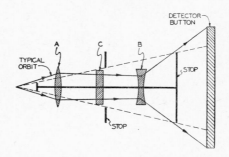

Fig. 8. Ray diagram of the optical analogue of the radial focusing system.

In addition to the extensive data obtained by radioactive deposition there has been some excellent work done on several radioactive nuclei by methods which do not utilize the activity. The prime example of this is the work on Cs^{134}, Cs^{135}, Cs^{137} by Stroke, Jaccarino, Edmonds, and Weiss,[24] who used surface ionization plus mass spectrometer detection.

Table 5 presents a summary of results obtained up to October 1, 1958, by atomic beam methods.

TABLE 5
SPINS OF RADIOACTIVE NUCLEI MEASURED BY ATOMIC BEAMS, OCTOBER 1, 1958

Nucleon Mass No.	Spin	References
H^3	1/2	Nelson and Nafe, *Phys. Rev.* **75**, 1194 (1949)
Na^2	3	Davis *et al.*, *Phys. Rev.* **76**, 1058 (1949)
K^{42}	2	Bellamy and Smith, *Phil. Mag.* **44**, 33 (1953)
K^{43}	3/2	H. Shugart, unpublished
Cu^{60}	2	Hooke, unpublished
Cu^{60}	2	Reynolds *et al.*, *Phys. Rev.* **109**, 465 (1958)
Cu^{61}	3/2	Nierenberg *et al.*, *Bull. Am. Phys. Soc.* **2**, 200 (1957)
Cu^{64}	1	Lemonick and Pipkin, *Phys. Rev.* **95**, 1356 (1954)
Ga^{66}	0	Hubbs *et al. Phys. Rev.* **105** 1928 (1957)
Ga^{67}	3/2	,, ,, ,, ,, ,, ,,
Ga^{68}	1	Hubbs *et al.*, *Phys. Rev.* **110**, 534 (1958)
Ga^{68}	1	Shugart, unpublished
As^{76}	2	Christenson *et al.*, *Phys. Rev.* **107**, 633 (1957)
Br^{82}	5	Green *et al.*, *Bull. Am. Phys. Soc.* **2**, 383 (1957)
Rb^{81}	3/2	Hubbs *et al.*, *Phys. Rev.* **107**, 723 (1957)
Rb^{81m}	9/2	,, ,, ,, ,, ,, ,,
Rb^{82}	5	,, ,, ,, ,, ,, ,,
Rb^{83}	5/2	,, ,, ,, ,, ,, ,,
Rb^{84}	2	,, ,, ,, ,, ,, ,,
Rb^{86}	2	Bellamy and Smith, *Phil. Mag.* **44**, 33 (1953)
Ag^{104}	2	Hamilton, unpublished
Ag^{104}	2	Reynolds *et al.*, *Phys. Rev.* **109**, 465 (1958)
Ag^{105}	1/2	Shugart, unpublished
$Ag^{106}(8.6d)$	6	Hamilton, unpublished
$Ag^{106}(24 min)$	1	Hamilton, unpublished
$Ag^{106}(8.6d)$	6	Reynolds *et al.*, *Phys. Rev.* **109**, 465 (1958)
$Ag^{106}(24 min)$	1	,, ,, ,, ,, ,,
Ag^{110m}	6	Eubank *et al.*, *Bull. Am. Phys. Soc.* **2**, 317 (1957)
Ag^{110m}	6	Ewbank *et al.*, *Phys. Rev.* **110**, 595 (1958)
Ag^{111}	1/2	Lemonick and Pipkin, *Phys. Rev.* **95**, 1356 (1954)
In^{109}	9/2	Marino *et al.*, *Phys. Rev.* **111**, 286 (1958)
In^{110}	7	,, ,, ,, ,, ,, ,,
In^{111}	9/2	,, ,, ,, ,, ,, ,,
In^{113m}	1/2	Childs and Goodman, *Bull. Am. Phys. Soc.* **1**, 342 (1956)
In^{114m}	5	Goodman and Wexler, *Phys. Rev.* **100**, 1796, 1245 (1955)
In^{116m}	5	Goodman and Wexler, *Phys. Rev.* **100**, 1796 (1955)

TABLE 5 (CONTD.)

Nucleon Mass No.	Spin	References
I^{123}	5/2	Lipworth, *Bull. Am. Phys. Soc.* **2**, 316 (1957)
I^{124}	2	Garvin *et al.*, *Bull. Am. Phys. Soc.* **2**, 383 (1957)
I^{128}	1	Sherwood, unpublished
I^{130}	5	Garvin *et al.*, *Phys. Rev. Let.* **1**, 292 (1958)
I^{131}	7/2	Garvin *et al.*, *Phys. Rev.* **111**, 534 (1958)
I^{131}	7/2	Lipworth, unpublished
Cs^{127}	1/2	Silsbee *et al.*, *Bull Am. Phys. Soc.* **2**, 30 (1957)
Cs^{129}	1/2	,, ,, ,, ,, ,, ,, ,,
Cs^{130}	1	Nierenberg *et al.*, *Phys. Rev.* **104**, 1380 (1956)
Cs^{131}	5/2	Bellamy and Smith, *Phil. Mag.* **44**, 33 (1953)
Cs^{132}	2	Nierenberg *et al.*, *Bull. Am. Phys. Soc.* **1**, 343 (1956)
Cs^{134}	4	Stroke *et al.*, *Phys. Rev.* **105**, 590 (1957)
$Cs^{134\,m}$	8	Goodman and Wexler, Cohen and Gilbert, *Phys. Rev.* **97**, 243 (1955)
Cs^{135}	7/2	Stroke *et al.*, *Phys. Rev.* **105**, 590 (1957)
Cs^{137}	7/2	,, ,, ,, ,, ,, ,, ,,
Au^{191}	3/2	Eubank *et al.*, *Bull. Am. Phys. Soc.* **2**, 383 (1957)
Au^{192}	1	,, ,, ,, ,, ,, ,, ,, ,,
Au^{193}	3/2	,, ,, ,, ,, ,, ,, ,, ,,
Au^{194}	1	Hooke *et al.*, *Bull. Am. Phys. Soc.* **2**, 317 (1957)
Au^{196}	2	Shugart, unpublished
Au^{198}	2	Christenson *et al.*, *Phys. Rev.* **101**, 1389 (1956)
Au^{199}	3/2	,, ,, ,, ,, ,, ,, ,, ,,
Tl^{197}	1/2	Shugart, Brink *et al.*, *Phys. Rev.* **107**, 189 (1957)
$Tl^{198\,m}$	7	,, ,, ,, ,, ,,, ,, ,, ,,
Tl^{199}	1/2	,, ,, ,, ,, ,, ,, ,, ,,
Tl^{204}	2	,, ,, ,, ,, ,, ,, ,,
Bi^{203}	9/2	Lindgren and Johansen (to be published in *Nuclear Physics*)
Bi^{204}	6	,, ,, ,, ,, ,, ,, ,, ,, ,,
Bi^{205}	9/2	,, ,, ,, ,, ,, ,, ,, ,, ,,
Bi^{206}	6	,, ,, ,, ,, ,, ,, ; Shugart, unpublished
Bi^{210}	1	K. F. Smith, *Physica* **18**, 989 (1952)
At^{211}	9/2	Garvin *et al.*, *Phys. Rev. Let.* **1**, 74 (1958)
Np^{238}	2	Hubbs and Marrus, *Phys. Rev.* **110**, 287 (1958)
Np^{239}	5/2	Albridge *et al.*, *Phys. Rev.* **111**, 1137 (1958)
Pu^{239}	1/2	Hubbs *et al.*, *Phys. Rev.* **109**, 390 (1958)
Pu^{239}	1/2	Hubbs *et al.*, *Bull. Am. Phys. Soc.* **2**, 316 (1957)
Am^{241}	5/2	Hubbs, unpublished
Cm^{242}	0	Hubbs *et al.*, *Phys. Rev.*, to appear March 1959

In the interest of simplicity only the spins are listed in this table. Since interpretation of magnetic moments data depends upon the method of measurement and the various theoretical corrections which must be applied to the experimental data, the original references must be consulted where precise values of the moments are required. Extensive magnetic moment data is listed in some previously published tables.[27]

Conclusion

The use of radioactive detection is a powerful tool in the method of atomic beams for nuclear spin and moment determinations. If one is willing to make extensive tests to obtain the proper target for deposition, using liquid He if necessary, this detection method should be applicable to nearly all radioactive nuclides.

Among the difficulties of extending the atomic beam field is the problem of producing a beam of atoms of refractory elements. Some significant progress has been made recently by the Berkeley group in working with Np and Am.[28] Such materials as the Pt group might conceivably be vaporized by plating on a tungsten wire and then flashing it. In this manner the wire would replace the oven and one would probably require a fresh wire for each observation.

The atomic beam method is not readily applicable to elements for which the ground state is a singlet. In principle one might use very strong gradient A and B fields, such as have been used in beam studies on molecules in which the net magnetic moment is of the order of a nuclear magneton. Such an apparatus would necessarily be much less efficient in the use of material because of the narrower slits and longer beam. No one has yet attempted such an experiment.

The technique of atomic beams is extremely productive, having yielded approximately 50 spins, most of them in the past two years. This method is still not universal, and one must recognize that the methods of optical spectroscopy as well as paramagnetic resonance must be utilized further in the study of ground state moments of the radioactive nuclei.

REFERENCES

[1] G. Breit and I. I. Rabi, *Phys. Rev.* **38**, 2082 (1931).
[2] I. I. Rabi and V. W. Cohen, *Phys. Rev.* **43**, 582 (1933).
[3] V. W. Cohen, *Phys. Rev.* **46**, 713 (1934).
[4] H. Kopfermann, *Z. Physik* **73**, 437 (1932).
[5] Jackson, *Proc. Roy. Soc.* A **143**, 455 (1933).
[6] W. M. Harrison and J. G. Hamilton, *Chem. Rev.*, Oct. 1, 1951.
[7] C. H. Townes and A. L. Schawlow, "Microwave Spectroscopy," McGraw-Hill, New York, 1955.
[8] Burke, Strandberg, Cohen, and Koski, *Phys. Rev.* **93**, 193 (1954).
[9] C. Kikuchi and R. D. Spence, *Am. J. Phys.* **18**, 167 (1950).

[10] B. Bleaney and K. W. S. Stevens, *Reports on Progress in Physics*, XVI (1953).
[11] Kikuchi, Sirvetz and Cohen, *Phys. Rev.* **92**, 109 (1953).
[12] Pake, Weissman, and Townsend, *Discuss. Faraday Soc.*, No. 19, p. 147, 1955.
[13] R. C. Fletcher, W. A. Yager, G. L. Pearson and F. R. Merritt, *Phys. Rev.* **95**, 844 (1954).
[14] G. Feher, *Phys. Rev.* **103**, 834 (1956).
[15] G. Feher, Fuller, and Gere, *Phys. Rev.* **107**, 1463 (1957).
[16] C. D. Jeffries, *Phys. Rev.* **106**, 164 (1957).
[17] Pipkin and Culvahouse, *Phys. Rev.* **106**, 1102 (1957).
[18] Abraham, Kedzie, and Jeffries, *Phys. Rev.* **106**, 165 (1957).
[19] Smith and Bellamy, *Phil. Mag.* **44**, 33 (1953).
[20] In England: Oxford, Cambridge.
In Germany: University of Bonn.
In Sweden: University of Upsala.
In United States: Argonne National Laboratory, Brookhaven National Laboratory, Oak Ridge National Laboratory, Princeton University, University of California.
[21] The equation generally referred to as the Breit-Rabi equation was first given by Kusch, Millman, and Rabi, *Phys. Rev.* **57**, 765 (1940) and represents the original Breit-Rabi equation of Reference 1 with added terms in g_i.
[22] E. Fermi and E. Segrè, *Z. Physik* **60**, 320 (1930).
[23] A. Bohr and V. W. Weisskopf, *Phys. Rev.* **77**, 94 (1950).
[24] Stroke, Jaccarino, Edmonds, and Weiss, *Phys. Rev.* **105**, 590 (1957).
[25] H. Friedburg and W. Paul, *Naturwiss.* **38**, 159 (1951).
[26] Lemonick and Pipkin, *Phys. Rev.* **95**, 1356 (1954).
[27] N. F. Ramsey, "Nuclear Moments," Wiley, New York, (1953); H. E. Walchli, "A Table of Nuclear Moment Data," Oak Ridge National Laboratory, Oak Ridge, Tenn., Index No. ORNL 1469 (1953), and Supp. No. 2 (1955); W. A. Nierenberg, *Annual Rev. of Nuclear Science*, 1958 (in press).
[28] J. C. Hubbs, *Bull. Am. Phys. Soc.* II, **2**, 316 (1957) and private communication on Am.

8

Molecular Scattering at the Solid Surface

F. C. HURLBUT
University of California, Berkeley, California

I. Introduction

From the days of its first development the molecular beam has been recognized as a powerful tool in the study of gas-surface interactions. Such investigations in great measure were stimulated and given momentum by the early work of Stern and his associates. This classic period was climaxed, although by no means terminated, by the work of Estermann and Stern[1] in studies of the diffraction of helium atoms and hydrogen molecules at surfaces of cleaved crystals. Within recent times, and concurrent with the considerable advances made in the kinetic theory as applied to the mechanics of rarefied gases, interest in the physics of interaction at the gas-surface interface has become renewed and the molecular beam has once again been applied to the study of these problems. For the most part these studies have been undertaken with the broad objective of supplying the microscopic detail of momentum and energy exchange between the directed particle and the surface. The present paper describes a series of such studies recently undertaken at the University of California,* and discusses the consequences of the findings to fluid friction in a rarefied gas flow.

II. Experimental

The work was conducted in an apparatus resembling, in much of the external detail, one of the more conventional atomic beam equipments. The essentials of the system are indicated in Figs. 1a and 1b. In addition to the elements illustrated, the equipment contained many of the familiar components of vacuum technology, oil vapor diffusion pumps, refrigerated traps, monitoring gages, and a gas supply system. The axi-symmetric configuration of Fig. 1a was chosen to permit observations of the scattered molecule flux at any position on the

* These studies have been supported for the past several years by a joint program of the Office of Naval Research and the Office of Scientific Research, U.S. Air Force.

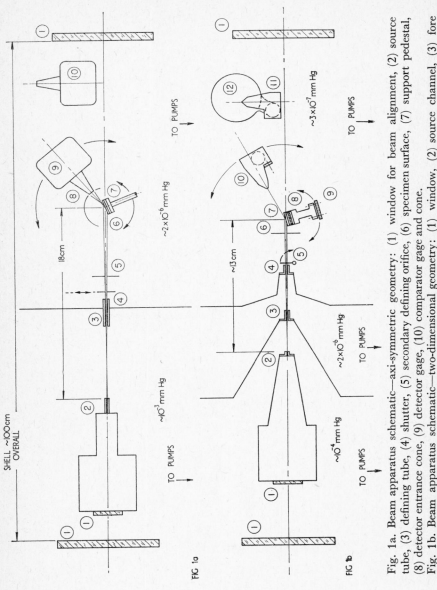

Fig. 1a. Beam apparatus schematic—axi-symmetric geometry: (1) window for beam alignment, (2) source tube, (3) defining tube, (4) shutter, (5) secondary defining orifice, (6) specimen surface, (7) support pedestal, (8) detector entrance cone, (9) detector gage, (10) comparator gage and cone.

Fig. 1b. Beam apparatus schematic—two-dimensional geometry: (1) window, (2) source channel, (3) fore channel, (4) defining channel, (5) shutter, (6) secondary defining slit, (7) specimen surface, (8) heater, (9) support pedestal, (10) detector head, (11) comparator head, (12) comparator gage.

available hemisphere including, therefore, observations at positions out of the incident plane. The angular aperture of the detector was fixed at 0.005 steradians by considerations of the minimum resolvable signal, the cone angle being therefore approximately 0.3 radians. The source was unheated, and no fore-slit was employed, the necessary pressure ratios between regions being maintained by long defining tubes of low conductance. In the test region the target specimen was supported in such a way as to provide arbitrary orientation of specimen and detector with respect to the incident beam (Fig. 2). Immediately preceding the target specimen was fixed a thin-edged orifice serving as a final stop in the geometrical definition of the beam.

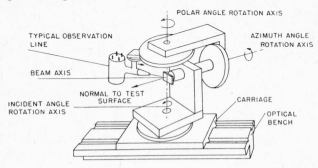

SCHEMATIC OF BASIC ROTATION ELEMENTS
OF DETECTOR MECHANISM

Fig. 2

The two-dimensional geometry, Fig. 1b, was employed in the most recent studies in order to permit the performance of a higher resolution experiment, particularly in respect to measurement near glancing incidence. It was found to be desirable in this case to introduce the region of differential pumping illustrated, and to make certain refinements in the pumping and trapping system. It was found possible to reduce the plane angle subtended by the detector slit to 0.01 radians.

The ionization gage was selected for development as the molecular beam detector in this apparatus because of its high sensitivity and its relative freedom from thermal instabilities. As in the more familiar Pirani detection system, the measurement cycle is initiated by withdrawal of the shutter, the beam strikes the target and scattered molecules fill the reservoir of the gage. Also, as in the Pirani system, a comparator gage performs the necessary background pressure measurement. The problem in such a system lies in the maintenance of

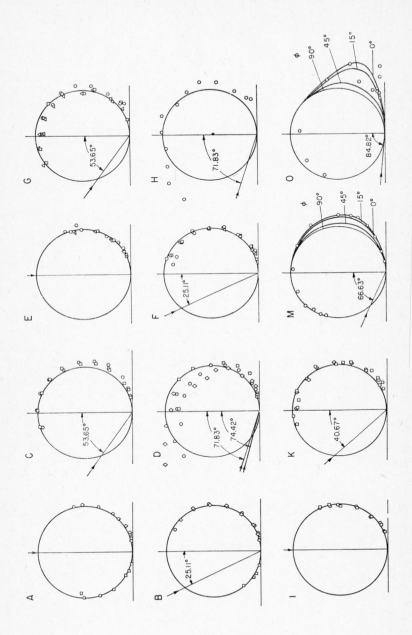

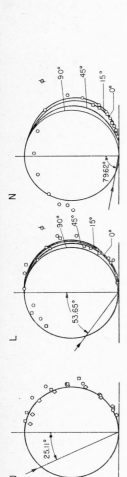

Fig. 3. Polar plots of the scattering data—axi-symmetric geometry.

Plot	Surface		Incident angle	Azimuth angle	Symbol	Date
A	Polished steel		0.00°	0.00°	○	2-15-53
			0.00°	0.00°	□	2-17-53
			0.00°	19.57°	◇	2-21-53
B	Polished steel		25.11°	0.00°	○	2-15-53
			25.11°	0.00°	□	2-17-53
			25.11°	19.57°	◇	2-21-53
C	Polished steel		53.65°	15.94°	□	2-26-53
			53.65°	0.00°	○	2-27-53
D	Polished steel		71.83°	15.94°	◇	2-26-53
			74.42°	15.94°	□	2-24-53
			71.83°	0.00°	○	2-27-53
E	Polished aluminum	unheated	0.00°	0.00°	○	3-23-53
		heated	0.00°	0.00°	□	4- 7-53
		unheated	0.00°	0.00°	△	4- 8-53
F	Polished aluminum	unheated	25.11°	0.00°	○	3-23-53
		heated	25.11°	0.00°	□	4- 7-53
		unheated	25.11°	0.00°	△	4- 8-53
G	Polished aluminum	unheated	53.65°	0.00°	○	3-23-53
		heated	53.65°	0.00°	□	4- 7-53
		unheated	53.65°	0.00°	△	4- 8-53
H	Polished aluminum	unheated	71.83°	0.00°	○	3-23-53
I	Unpolished glass		0.00°	0.00°	□	5-16-53
			0.00°	19.57°	○	5-23-53
J	Unpolished glass		25.11°	0.00°	○	5-16-53
			25.11°	0.00°	◇	5- 5-53
			25.11°	19.57°	□	5-17-53
K	Unpolished glass		40.67°	0.00°	○	5-16-53
			40.67°	15.58°	◇	5-23-53
			40.67°	35.83°	○	5-25-53
L	Unpolished glass		53.65°	0.00°	○	5-16-53
			53.65°	0.00°	□	6-18-53
M	Unpolished glass		66.63°	0.00°	○	6-20-53
N	Unpolished glass		79.62°	0.00°	○	6-21-53
			79.62°	15.58°	□	5-23-53
O	Unpolished glass		84.82°	0.00°	○	6-21-53

sufficiently stable electron emission at the ionization gage cathode. For the purpose of these studies emission regulators and a difference detector* were developed which permitted resolution of signals to less than 10^{-10} mm Hg in the presence of fluctuations in the background pressures of the order of 10^{-8} mm Hg. In the case of the axi-symmetric system with a path length of the order of 18 cm, background pressure within the beam chamber was approximately 2×10^{-6} mm Hg, and the maximum pressure increments within the gage due to the influx of the scattered beam were of the order of 10^{-9} mm Hg. In the two-dimensional configuration with a somewhat shorter path length and higher resolution detector geometry, the scattered beam pressure increments are of the same order in the presence of background pressures of the order of 3×10^{-7} mm Hg.

The first sequence of studies was performed with the axi-symmetric geometry employing beams of nitrogen and surfaces of cold rolled steel and of aluminum prepared by conventional metallurgical polishing. Similar surfaces polished and then etched in the conventional manner, and surfaces of common window glass both "as cooled" and optically polished were also used. Precautions were taken to insure cleanliness of the test surfaces within the limitations imposed by the apparatus. The metal surfaces were heated in some instances, but were not consistently degassed, nor were they held at elevated temperature for all traverses. The glass surfaces were not heated in the course of these experiments. Polar representations of the data are presented in Fig. 3, and dates and descriptive material relative to the plots appear in the caption below.

The ambiguities stemming from the non-uniformity of surface history were in part removed in the two-dimensional studies by the use of a small radiant heater mounted just beneath the surface within the support pedestal. By means of this heater it was possible to degas the surface before each run and then maintain it at approximately 100° C for the balance of the running period. Polished glass and Teflon were used as the target specimens, while air, nitrogen and argon were used as the beam gas. Only the glass surface was degassed in this series. Representative polar plots of the experimental results are presented in Fig. 4.

III. Discussion

An inspection of the polar representations of the data reveals the salient feature of the findings; by far the greatest number of molecules are scattered at random, as from an ideally rough surface, for all

* An Ionization Detection System for Molecular Beams. (To be published.)

combinations of gas and surface. The measured flux distributions adhere closely to the cosine or "diffuse" scattering pattern and show no sharp perturbation of that pattern; no "specular" lobes are observed. On the other hand, there is in evidence a small, although measurable, departure from cosine scattering in the cases of the glass and Teflon surfaces. In these cases, and the data of 1957 for glass repeated that of 1953 in this respect, a small fraction of the incident molecules was scattered into directions lying about the specular ray in addition to that expected on the basis of a purely random distribution. Furthermore, in the case of the glass surfaces it would appear that the fraction so scattered increased with increasing angle of incidence, although to the limiting angle of the experiment, about 89.5° in the more recent case, no evidence was obtained of a sharper form of specular scattering.

There is a substantial resemblance between these data and those of Zahl[2] and Josephy,[3] obtained in studies of the scattering of Hg from cleaved NaCl crystals. The specular fraction in these cases, however, was of much greater magnitude than the diffuse. Zahl reported complete diffuse scattering of Hg from glass. A point of distinction between the data of Zahl and those of the present studies with glass is found in the constancy of the amplitude of the specular lobe in Zahl's case at all incident angles even near normal incidence. On the other hand, it is just here that the observations of scattering from the Teflon surface may be found to differ from those involving glass. An inspection of Fig. 4 reveals a distortion of the cosine distribution in the Teflon studies which persists to substantially smaller angles of incidence than in the other case.

It is difficult on the basis of the present observations to go far toward the formulation of theories of interaction or even toward the precise characterization of the surface itself. It would seem likely that the best language with which to discuss these matters remains for the present that of classical physics. In these terms it would appear that the surface is rough on a molecular scale, a not unexpected conclusion. It is known from studies of energy accommodation at surfaces[4] that the adjustment in energy is much less completely accomplished in general than the adjustment of momentum, as may be judged from the present experiment. It has frequently been argued that all interactions are more or less specular, in that they involve a sticking time or time of adsorption at the surface which is short by comparison with the time needed for the adjustment of molecular energy to that of the surface, but that the molecule is trapped in fissures and in the mean makes several collisions with the surface. It may require numerous

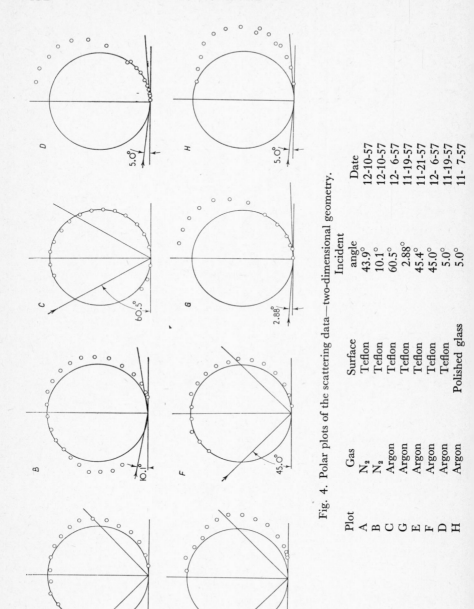

Fig. 4. Polar plots of the scattering data—two-dimensional geometry.

Plot	Gas	Surface	Incident angle	Date
A	N_2	Teflon	43.9°	12-10-57
B	N_2	Teflon	10.1°	12-10-57
C	Argon	Teflon	60.5°	12- 6-57
G	Argon	Teflon	2.88°	11-19-57
E	Argon	Teflon	45.4°	11-21-57
F	Argon	Teflon	45.0°	12- 6-57
D	Argon	Teflon	5.0°	11-19-57
H	Argon	Polished glass	5.0°	11- 7-57

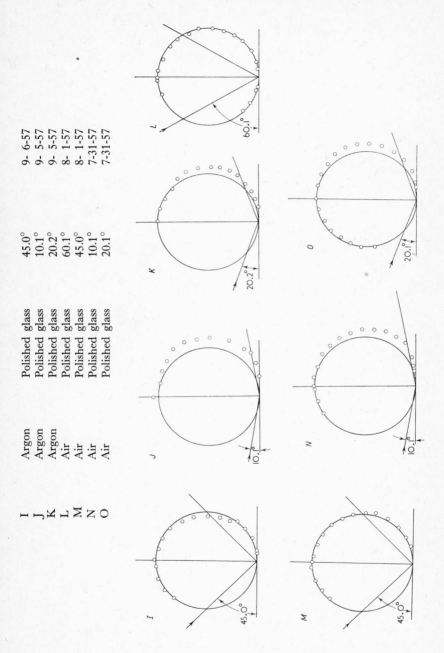

I	Argon	Polished glass	45.0°	9- 6-57
J	Argon	Polished glass	10.1°	9- 5-57
K	Argon	Polished glass	20.2°	9- 5-57
L	Air	Polished glass	60.1°	8- 1-57
M	Air	Polished glass	45.0°	8- 1-57
N	Air	Polished glass	10.1°	7-31-57
O	Air	Polished glass	20.1°	7-31-57

collisions, in that view, to accomplish a complete adjustment in energy, but only one or two to accomplish the observed loss of influence of the incident trajectory. Such an argument has a certain plausibility in the case of reasonably clean and degassed surfaces as in the second sequence of experiments reported here, although it would not be expected to apply in the case of single crystal surfaces. These remarks have been made at this length only in order to make plain that the present studies shed no light on the details of energy accommodation at the surface. Both the "specular" and the "diffuse" interactions may have occurred without energy exchange, or equally well with some adjustment in energy toward that of a gas at the surface temperature.

It is interesting to consider to what extent the above difficulty may be resolved by the examination of experiment in the field of rarefied gas flow and to obtain in this process some understanding of the consequences of these results to fluid friction in such flows. Two gas-surface interaction parameters are commonly employed in the formulation of boundary conditions for rarefied gas flows and are discussed in textbooks on kinetic theory as the coefficient of momentum transfer, f (coefficient of specular reflection), and the coefficient of energy accommodation, α. It is with the first of these coefficients that we shall be concerned here. This coefficient was proposed by Maxwell and discussed in terms of a fraction $1 - f$ of molecules specularly reflected in interaction with the surface, and a fraction f diffusely reflected. In a near equilibrium flow of a gas past a surface one may identify the quantity f defined in this manner with f defined as that fraction of the incident tangential momentum which is transferred to the surface in the momentum exchange. We may write

$$f = \frac{G_i - G_r}{G_i} \tag{1}$$

in which G_i is the magnitude of the tangential momentum brought to the surface by all incident molecules, and G_r is that which is transferred to the issuing molecules by the surface. Conservation in molecular number density at the surface is assumed.

It has been shown[5] in the case of a rarefied gas in laminar flow parallel to a surface that one may calculate the value of f in accordance with Eq. (1) where the interaction details necessary to the calculation of G_r are supplied from molecular beam experiment. In order to complete the calculation where only information relating to the angular distributions in the scattered flux is available from experiment, assumptions must be made relating to the nature of the exchange of energy at the surface. Two limiting assumptions are available: (1) that the specular component, i.e. those molecules appearing in the specular lobe in excess of the number expected on the basis of diffuse scattering, is completely adjusted in energy to that of a gas in equilibrium at the temperature of the surface, and (2), that the specular component is totally unadjusted in energy and retains in consequence the energy of its initial trajectory. One may then characterize the assumed rarefied gas flow of this calculation by means of s, the molecular speed ratio, where

$$ s = \frac{U}{V_m} \qquad (2) $$

where U is the mass velocity of the gas flow and V_m is the most probable thermal speed of the molecules. It can be seen that as U becomes large with respect to V_m a predominance of momentum will be incident on the surface at angles close to glancing. Where the flux of molecules comprising the specular component is in part a function of the angle of incidence of the molecule on the surface, one can see that the calculated value of f will in general be a function of the parameter s. Calculations on the basis of both extremal assumptions for the case of the nitrogen-glass interaction have been carried out and the results are presented in Fig. 5.

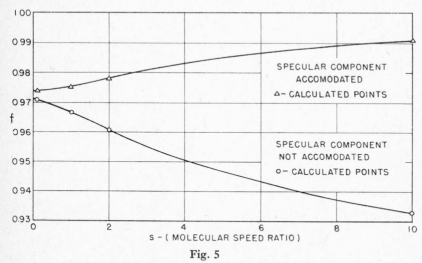

Fig. 5

It is seen that as the relative speed of gas and surface increases the value of f decreases in the case of assumption (2). By means of friction drag studies in rarefied gas flows, as might be performed in a rotating cylinder apparatus one might well determine which of the limiting assumptions lies closer to reality, provided adequate surface cleanliness could be assured and suitable values of s achieved. A somewhat more immediate result of this calculation lies in the realization that very large and readily discernable lobes would be required if calculated values of f substantially below 1 were to result. Thus, calculations of aerodynamic forces on bodies in rarefied atmospheres which have been made on the assumption that f can be taken as unity for practical purposes can be seen to rest on a reasonable experimental footing. One should guard very carefully, however, against an uncritical extrapolation of these results for low interaction energies to calculations involving interaction energies of the order of 1 to 10 electron volts. Much work must yet be done before sufficient experience has been gained either for the formulation of theories of the interaction or even for gas mechanic prediction where the interaction energies of particle and surface are high.

REFERENCES

[1] I. Estermann and O. Stern, *Z. Physik* **61**, 95 (1930).

[2] H. A. Zahl and A. Ellet, *Phys. Rev.* **38**, 977 (1931).

[3] B. Josephy, *Z. Physik* **80**, 755 (1933).

[4] L. B. Loeb, *Kinetic Theory of Gases*, p. 301 (1927 and 1934), and E. H. Kennard, *Kinetic Theory of Gases* (1938).

[5] F. C. Hurlbut, "Studies of Molecular Scattering at the Solid Surface," *J. Appl. Phys.* **28**, No. 8, 844–850 (1957).

9

Some Applications of Molecular Beam Techniques to Chemistry

SHELDON DATZ and ELLISON H. TAYLOR

Chemistry Division, Oak Ridge National Laboratory, Oak Ridge, Tennessee

Introduction

Although the contributions of molecular beams to physics far out-shadow those to chemistry, there are enough of the latter to merit a separate review (some chemical studies are included in more general reviews.[1,2,3,4]) For the present purposes, molecular beam experiments in chemistry are considered to fall into three classes:

    (1) Measurement of atomic and molecular properties.

    (2) Sampling of chemical systems.

    (3) Study of molecular collisions.

Category (1), the measurement of energy levels, moments, polarizabilities, etc., will be omitted as being properly physics, although the results are often of use in chemical problems. Category (2) is treated only in outline. Although the results are of great chemical interest (vapor pressures, heats of association, evidence for transitory intermediates, etc.) the utilization of beam techniques is usually elementary. Category (3) is treated extensively since it is probably the one in which the molecular beam method can make its greatest contribution to chemistry. Diffraction experiments are only mentioned, and the subject of elastic collisions is treated in outline, but the coverage of other topics is intended to be essentially complete.

Sampling of Chemical Systems

Freedom from collision is obtained in a molecular beam by maintaining at the source the conditions of pressure and orifice dimensions which ensure effusive flow. Whether the effusing molecules are collimated to a beam or not, the absence of collisions beyond the orifice makes those molecules in many cases a representative sample of the system in the source. Thus the flux of molecules is proportional to the concentration in the source, the composition of the beam (corrected for effusive mass separation) is a sample of the vapor composition, and the distribution of the energy among the molecules of the beam corresponds to that of the vapor, except for the modified distribution of translational energy (and barring emission or absorption of radiation outside the orifice). Also, if the source is a reacting gas mixture, an effusing beam may contain detectable amounts of transitory intermediates.

The first example of such sampling by a collimated beam appears to have been Stern's experiment on velocity distribution,[5] carried out in 1920. Later experiments have provided data of direct chemical interest. Improvements in resolution have permitted the analysis of the composite velocity distribution of beams containing polymeric species, and thus the measurement of the degree and, by temperature variation, of the heat of vapor association.[6,7,8] Diamagnetic dimeric molecules in a vapor of paramagnetic atoms may be analyzed magnetically to the same end.[9,10]

Measurement of vapor pressure by effusive sampling (without collimation) predates the complete molecular beam technique, going back to the work of Knudsen.[11] The variations that have been used go all the way from true, collimated molecular beams to a simple heated wire in vacuo.[12] The particular advantage of effusive sampling appears at high temperatures, where materials for other types of manometers are lacking. An extreme example is the determination of the heat of sublimation of carbon,[13] and the numerous experiments on this subject attest also to the principal difficulty of the method, the necessity for knowledge of the species in the vapor.

If one component is non-volatile[14] or can be distinguished from the others,[15] partial vapor pressures may be measured, and the relevant partial thermodynamic quantities for solid or liquid solutions determined.

The sampling of equilibrium systems in this way is now so well-established that the principal interest is in the various thermodynamic quantities thus determined, and their relation to other chemical variables. More than this outline would therefore be out of place.

The sampling by effusion of reacting systems is less well-developed, largely because of the difficulty of detecting and measuring the small quantities of short-lived species available. Also, the spectroscopic methods available for various species are often selective enough not to require isolation of the molecule (e.g. free-radical) from its environment. There are, however, many cases for which spectroscopic analysis *in situ* lacks the required sensitivity or selectivity. Mass spectroscopy offers high sensitivity and often good selectivity, and when applied to a reacting system almost always involves effusive sampling. This method was first applied to thermal reactions and to flames, by Eltenton.[16] It has been used in photochemistry, both with steady illumination,[17] and recently, with rapid mass scanning, for following flash photolysis.[18] Catalytic reactions have also been studied.[19] The most thorough-going adoption of the molecular beam technique for this purpose is the work of Foner and Hudson,[20] in which a collimated, modulated beam is the sample for the mass spectrometer. Improvements in details of the technique may make possible in-flight separation of excited states and measurement of energies of stable products to add wanted details to our knowledge of reaction mechanisms. The complications attendant on the multiple-collision source make the interpretation in fine detail more difficult than with reactions between crossed molecular beams, but the results for that same reason are more directly representative of the situation in ordinary gaseous reactions.

Molecular Collisions

The essence of chemistry is chemical reaction, and it has been realized for at least thirty years[21] that the molecular collisions which lead to reaction could be studied almost ideally by molecular beams. The principal obstacle to such studies has been the problem of detection, and this has been severe enough that only a few actual reaction studies have been attempted under beam conditions. Experiments with less specific chemical requirements, such as elastic scattering, have been more tractable, and the results have important application to the macroscopic properties of gases as well as to intermolecular forces. Collision experiments in which one component is a solid surface are made easier by the higher rate and the sharp localization of the collisions, and a variety of chemically interesting experiments has been performed in this field. Because of the wide use of the surface ionization gage in molecular beam work, gas-surface interactions resulting in ionization are particularly interesting.

Gas-Surface Interactions

In studies of the interaction of gas molecules with solid surfaces, molecular beam techniques can be used in many cases to simplify experimental conditions and the interpretation of results. It is desirable to be able to observe the consequences of single collisions of particles in well defined energy states with uncontaminated surfaces of known composition and temperature, conditions closely approximated if the gas source is a molecular beam and the solid surface is maintained in a high vacuum.

Studies of diffraction of molecular beams from crystal surfaces have confirmed the concept of the associated de Broglie wavelength. The observation of anomalous behavior in the diffraction of inert gases from alkali halide lattices has led to a theory of selective van der Waals adsorption which has had wide application to this type of adsorption phenomenon.[22] This work has been well recorded and summarized in books by Fraser[1] and Massey and Burhop.[23]

Fraser also summarized the beam experiments done prior to 1931 on reflection, adsorption, condensation, and surface migration. The chemists' interest in these fields lies primarily in the forces involved in energy exchange, chemisorption, nucleation and surface catalysis. It should be noted that the theoretical explanation of these phenomena, with the possible exception of those involving simple van der Waals interaction,[24] is still in a considerable state of flux and only in recent years have the experimental techniques been developed to the extent where some quantitative information has become available. The principal difficulty has always been in obtaining truly clean surfaces since the effect of even a monolayer of adsorbate is sometimes sufficient to mask the true nature of the substrate. For example, in condensation from the gas phase there are two distinct types of interaction. If the heat of adsorption is large, as in the case of a metal atom on a metallic surface, the surface mobility is small and deposition may take place uniformly without exhibiting any critical phenomena. If, on the other hand, the surface-adsorbate interaction is small, as would be the case of a metal atom on a metal surface covered by adsorbed gas, surface mobility exists and nucleation is required for observable condensation, i.e. there may exist a critical flux below which no condensation can occur.

For investigating metal-metal interactions, Yang, Simnad and Pound[25] used a radio-tracer technique to measure the condensation coefficients of an atomic silver beam on four metallic substrates. They found that the coefficients varied from 1.0 on silver to 0.64 on nickel and that these coefficients could be related almost linearly to the lattice mismatch of the silver atom to the substrate lattice. In another paper by Yang and co-workers,[26] the effect of substrate disregistry on the nucleation of sodium crystals was not too well demonstrated, although the effect did start to appear as the surface temperature was increased, perhaps indicating desorption of a contaminant.

The effect of surface impurities was also demonstrated by Frauen-felder,[27] using radio-tracer detection. He showed that the condensation coefficients of cadmium and mercury on metallic surfaces could be changed from less than 0.01 on a mechanically cleaned surface to approximately 0.3 on a freshly evaporated surface, in agreement with the earlier qualitative observations of Cockroft[28] on cadmium. How-ever, the condensation coefficient for silver changed only slightly, from 0.3–0.6 on a mechanically cleaned surface to 0.4–0.8 on the evaporated film. Copper gave coefficients of 0.4 to 0.6 on mechanically cleaned surfaces. It is interesting to note, both from this work and from that of Yang *et al.*, the contrast between the condensation coeffi-cients of silver and copper, which appear almost independent of surface treatment, and those of cadmium, mercury, and sodium which depend strongly on the pretreatment. The former come from the oven at high temperature (in order to achieve the necessary vapor pressure), while the latter are obtained at relatively low temperature. It might, therefore, be conjectured that the reason for this difference in behavior is that the high-temperature atoms have sufficient kinetic energy to displace adsorbed gas molecules and interact directly with the surface while those formed at low temperature are adsorbed on the gas layer.

Further evidence for the effect of adsorbed gas on the condensation process may be found in the measured heats of adsorption. Frauen-felder[27] measured the heat of adsorption of cadmium on freshly deposited silver by measurement of the temperature dependence of the residence time of radio-cadmium, and obtained a value of 1.5–1.7 ev in qualitative agreement with valence bond theory. The earlier measurements of Estermann[29] and Cockroft[30] which gave the very low values of 0.13 and 0.25 ev, respectively, were probably affected by adsorbed contaminants, since they also found very low condensation coefficients.

The radio-tracer method has also been used by Devienne[31,32] for measurement of condensation coefficients of cadmium, antimony, and gold on various surfaces in varying states of purity. Although the results reported so far can hardly be considered quantitative, some of the methods used are noteworthy. For example, to determine the absolute coefficient independent of beam flux, the beam is directed through a small orifice into a chamber. The beam then impinges on the condensing surface at the end of the chamber, and the reflected atoms are ultimately caught on the wall. The condensation coefficient can then be obtained by measuring the relative radioactivity on the condensing surface and the wall. One interesting observation was a displacement of atoms from a previously deposited film of radio-antimony by a beam of non-radioactive antimony in a sort of sputtering effect.[33] Garin and Prugne[34] have reported some results on similar systems with somewhat more attention given to substrate preparation. Morgulis[35] has measured the condensation coefficient of strontium oxide containing Sr^{89} on degassed tungsten and found a value of 0.1 which increased with degree of surface coverage but was independent of the angle of incidence. References to other work in this field may be found in papers by Brewer,[36] Simpson,[37] and Wexler.[38]

A different technique was utilized by Bradley and Volans[39,40] in measuring the evaporation coefficient of potassium chloride from single crystals. (The condition of microscopic reversibility demands that the evaporation coefficient be identical to the condensation coefficient.) In this work the authors measured the rate of effusion of KCl vapor under two sets of conditions, first, through a small orifice where the rate is controlled by the vapor pressure, and second, without the orifice with the rate controlled by evaporation. They found the coefficients to be 0.72 for the (100) and (111) faces, and 0.56 for the (110) face. These coefficients exhibited no temperature dependence indicating that there was no activation energy for evaporation. This was somewhat unexpected since there is a 10% difference in the bond distance between solid and gas. The authors therefore postulated a mobile surface film with internuclear distance close to that of the gas. A difficulty in the quantitative interpretation of this work is the now questionable assumption that the KCl vapor is completely monomeric.[8] However, this method does give the desirable conditions of surface purity and crystal orientation.

Rates of surface migration of condensed atoms have been studied by Frank,[41] who measured the migration of cesium on tungsten oxide by observing the rate of decrease in photocurrent from a Cs beam deposit, and by Frauenfelder[27] who measured the spread of radioactivity from a sharply defined deposit of Cu^{64} on freshly evaporated silver.

The structure of the films formed by beam deposition and subsequent surface migration to nucleation sites has been a subject of study for several investigators. Evidence for these processes was first given by Estermann,[42] who subjected silver beam deposits to ultramicroscopic examination and found clusters of nuclei consisting of at least 1000 atoms. Cockroft[43] observed that condensed films exhibited colors characteristic of aggregates of small numbers of atoms. Johnson and Starky[44] measured the conductivity of deposits of mixed beams to determine the effect of occluded gas on deposition. In this work they condensed beams of mercury mixed with H_2, O_2, A, and CO_2. With H_2, O_2, and A the deposit gave evidence of random mixing of the Hg and occluded gas but with CO_2 and ionized O_2 there was evidence of formation of alternate layers. In another work Starky[45] observed the reflectivity of Cd deposits as a function of film growth and inferred some properties of the condensation process. The most direct work on the structure of such deposits has been that of Melnikova *et al.*,[46] who determined by x-ray analysis the orientation of crystallites of Mg, Zn, and Cd deposited from a beam. All of these metals crystallize in the hexagonal system. Using a widely divergent (30°) beam to give a wide range of angles of incidence, they demonstrated a definite correlation between the angle of incidence and the hexad axis of the crystallites. At the center, with normal incidence, the hexad axis was normal to the condensing surface. As the obliquity of incidence increased so did that of the hexad axis, but the latter was always more oblique than the angle of incidence. The magnitude of this effect was also found to vary with temperature. The application of this technique to studies of crystal growth habits may prove very fruitful.

In the field of surface catalysis, as in other branches of kinetics, the details of the molecular interactions have had to be inferred from the results of bulk experiments, complicated especially in this case by the problem of surface contamination. It has long been recognized that beam experiments would be of advantage here, but experimental difficulties have limited them. The first work utilizing beams in this manner was that of Alyea and Haber[47] who demonstrated that intersecting beams of hydrogen and oxygen did not react unless a silica surface was placed at the intersection point. Bodenstein[48] studied the catalytic combustion of ammonia on a platinum surface by directing a very low pressure stream of mixed gas at a heated platinum surface and freezing out the reaction product at liquid air temperature on the surrounding walls. Although the beams in these two works were not in the strictest sense internally collision free, the experiments are noteworthy in that they demonstrate what can be done in a beam study of two components on a surface.

Rice and Byck[49] studied the decomposition of molecular beams of acetone and of dimethyl mercury on heated platinum, tungsten, and tantalum. They observed no decomposition on platinum heated to 1600° C. If thermal equilibrium had been reached in the internal degrees of freedom, the decomposition of dimethyl mercury should have been observed. This result, therefore, indicates a low accommodation coefficient for internal energy transfer. On tantalum and tungsten surfaces, however, decomposition did occur with simultaneous formation of the metal carbide. This might be taken to indicate the necessity for a surface compound as an intermediate to give the high heat of adsorption necessary for long residence time and consequent transfer of internal energy.

A similar observation was made by Beeck,[50] who found no decomposition of pure hydrocarbon beams on a platinum filament at temperatures up to 1600° C, but he found that the addition of small amounts of water vapor or hydrogen sulfide to the beam caused reaction at much lower temperatures. Beeck[51] proposed that this effect was due to temporary adsorption of decomposition products of the additives, which activated the adsorption of the hydrocarbons. It is indeed unfortunate that these highly interesting preliminary experiments were never published in detail because it is impossible to evaluate the validity of some of the surprising conclusions.

In a recent communication, Dewing and Robertson[52] suggested the possibility of studying rates of fast, surface-catalyzed reactions by a beam method similar to the system used by Clausing[53] to measure surface residence times. In this experiment, a beam is directed normal to a spot on the surface of a high-speed rotating nickel disc. Molecules which are adsorbed on the disc are desorbed after traveling through an angle of rotation determined by their residence time and the angular velocity of the disc. To determine this angle, a tube is placed close to the disc surface at a variable lead angle to the impinging beam. If a molecule should evaporate into the tube, it is pumped away and collected. The system has been used for measuring residence times of hydrogen on nickel; at 19° C, the average lifetime after attaining steady state is 3×10^{-4} seconds. Since such short lifetimes are measurable, it seems probable that this method can be applied to studying single steps in heterogeneous reactions.

Further information about these processes can be obtained from a knowledge of the efficiency of internal energy transfer at the surface. Beeck[54] measured the accommodation coefficients of hydrocarbon molecules on nickel by passing a beam of known intensity into a calibrated Stern-Pirani gage. The true pressure in the cavity could be calculated from its geometry, and the "pressure" indicated by the gage was then a measure of the thermal conductivity of the gas. This method gives more accurate information than the usual thermal conductivity experiment since the very low pressures measurable in such a gage allow determination of the accommodation on a bare surface rather than on one which is already covered with adsorbate. However, since any thermal conductivity measurement gives the total energy transferred from the surface, this type of measurement alone cannot separate the relative contributions of translational and internal modes.

To distinguish between the efficiencies of energy transfer to translational and internal modes, Sasaki and co-workers[55] measured the total accommodation coefficient of nitrogen on nickel by a conventional thermal conductivity experiment, and attempted to measure separately the translational component by observation of the momentum transfer from a beam of nitrogen to a nickel vane of a silica torsion balance. Although, in principle, this method should give the desired information, it is doubtful if the sensitivity of a torsion balance is sufficient for this purpose.

Surface Ionization

A phenomenon that has been of great practical service to experimentation with molecular beams is surface ionization. Because ions can be measured with extreme sensitivity and because surface ionization proceeds at temperatures which provide clean surfaces, the study of the phenomenon itself can provide chemically interesting data under nearly ideal conditions. The theoretical treatment for equilibrium between a metal surface and an ionizable gas embodied in the Saha-Langmuir equation can be modified to apply to the beam-filament arrangement as follows.*

When an electropositive atom is adsorbed on a metallic surface it may give up an electron to the surface and become a positive ion. The equilibrium constant may be obtained from a knowledge of the standard free energy change, and therefore from the heat and entropy of ionization. It can be shown[59] that the heat of reaction in this case is given by the difference between the energy required to remove an electron from the atom and that required to remove it from the metal (i.e. the ionization potential, I, and the thermionic work function, φ). Since the concentration of electrons in the metal may be considered constant, the ratio of ions to atoms at the surface is given by

$$n_+/n_a = (\omega_+/\omega_a)e^{(\varphi-I)/kT} \tag{1}$$

where ω_+/ω_a, the ratio of statistical weights for ion and atom, is the only contribution from the entropy. This expression is valid only if thermodynamic equilibrium is attained. In the case of a beam of atoms impinging on a surface where reflection is possible, the ratio of positive ions (n_+) to incident atoms (n_i) becomes[60]

$$\frac{n_+}{n_i} = (1-r_i)\left[1 + \frac{\omega_a}{\omega_+}\left(\frac{1-r_a}{1-r_+}\right)\exp\left(\frac{-(\phi-I)}{kT}\right)\right]^{-1} \tag{2}$$

* More extensive treatments of the general theory may be found in works by Langmuir and Kingdon,[56] Becker[57] and Dobretzov.[58]

where r_i, r_a, and r_+ are reflection coefficients for incident atom, adsorbed atom and adsorbed ion, respectively. An identical expression can be derived for the process of negative surface ionization, in which an adsorbed electronegative atom may remove an electron from the surface to form a negative ion, the controlling factor in this case being the atom electron affinity, A, instead of the ionization potential. In the case of molecules striking a surface and dissociating, the observed ion current is characteristic of the atoms formed on the surface by decomposition.

The principal interest in surface ionization from the molecular beam standpoint has been in its use as a detector,[61] an application that has been well-summarized elsewhere.[4] The same qualities valuable here are of service also in the use of surface ionization sources for mass spectrometry.[62]

The use of this effect in studies of adsorption dates from the major work of Langmuir, Kingdon,[56] and Taylor[63] on cesium–tungsten. These experiments demonstrated very well the special qualities of surface ionization as a tool for the study of surface phenomena. Since positive-ion currents can be measured with great sensitivity, the method can follow surface coverage down to very low values. And, since the phenomenon occurs at high temperature on refractory metals, surface contamination can be minimized at quite modest vacua, for the fractional surface coverage, θ, is determined by the balance between incoming molecules (flux = n) and the rate of desorption characterized by the mean residence time, τ, according to

$$\theta = \tau n / N \tag{3}$$

where N is the number of adsorption sites. The coverage can therefore be reduced either by lowering the flux, by reducing the ambient pressure, or by lowering the residence time by raising the surface temperature, T, since

$$\tau = \tau_0 \, e^{\,\Delta H_a / kT} \tag{4}$$

where τ_0 is the period of vibration of the adsorbed molecule normal to the surface and ΔH_a is the heat of adsorption.[64]

The simplest system that can be studied by this method is the interaction of a metal atom with a surface. Since it has been demonstrated that the ion yield for all alkali metal atoms incident on a tungsten surface follows the Saha-Langmuir equation with no observed reflections,[60] time-dependent ion current measurements can be used to study directly the kinetics of these adsorption processes.

The first work of this type was done by Evans,[65] who exposed a heated tungsten surface to an alkali beam but maintained the electric field such that no ions could leave the surface. After steady state had been reached, the polarity was reversed and the positive ion current recorded on an oscillograph. Starodubtsev[66] and Knauer[67] used variations of a modulated beam technique in which the beam is pulsed by a rotating shutter, and the positive ion current displayed on an oscilloscope. The decay of the signal after the shutter has closed will indicate the residence time of the ion on the filament. As may be seen in Eq. (4), the ion current should decay exponentially, and a measurement of the mean residence time as a function of temperature will give an experimental heat of adsorption. A theoretical value can be calculated from the ionic radius, since in this case the heat of adsorption is due principally to the electrostatic attraction of the positive ion to a mirrored negative charge induced in the surface of the metal.[56] The results of the three different experiments and of the calculation are given in Table 1.

TABLE 1

HEATS OF ADSORPTION OF ALKALI METAL IONS ON TUNGSTEN

Ion	Ionic radius[68]	Calc.	Heat of adsorption (ev)		
			Evans	Starodubtsev	Knauer
Li^+	0.60	6.00	—	—	—
Na^+	0.95	3.79	—	3.3	—
K^+	1.33	2.70	2.43	2.55	2.9
Rb^+	1.48	2.43	2.14	—	—
Cs^+	1.69	2.13	1.81	—	3.6

The deviations of the results from theoretical values may be due either to experimental effects (as must certainly be the case for Knauer's value for Cs^+, since the energy should decrease with increasing radius) or to the presence of surface forces not taken into account in the simple theory. This subject is presently being studied by Hughes and Levinstein,[69] who have reported some preliminary results on the rubidium–tungsten system using a modulated beam technique on oriented single crystals of tungsten.

The behavior of the alkali metals on platinum was found by Datz and Taylor[60] to exhibit somewhat more complex behavior in that the ionization efficiency was less than that predicted from Eq. (1). This was attributed to a partial reflection of the incident atoms. The reflection coefficient (r_i) was shown to vary with the ionization potential of the alkali atom, increasing to a maximum at potassium and displaying a distinct minimum at sodium. The explanation advanced to explain these results is as follows. A high probability of electron transfer from the adatom into the metal exists only if there is an empty level in the surface states of the metal having an energy corresponding to the electronic ground state of the adatom. Platinum, with its outer electronic configuration of $6s\ 5d^9$, might be expected to possess only a few such levels. The minimum reflection at sodium may then correspond to a suitable vacancy in the platinum surface states, the maximum at potassium to a lower transition probability because of non-resonance with that vacancy, and the decline toward cesium either to approach to another vacancy, or to the increasing driving force associated with the decreasing ionization potential.

An unusual observation was made by Dobretzov and co-workers,[70] who measured the ionization efficiency of calcium and magnesium on thin films of their oxides on tungsten. Measurement of the temperature dependence of the electron emission from these wires indicated a work function very close to that of pure tungsten, but the ionization efficiency was found to be very much larger than the value expected from Eq. (1). Sodium and lead did not show a correspondingly high ionization efficiency, indicating an interesting chemical specificity, but lack of quantitative data precludes any detailed discussion.

For the surface ionization of the alkali halides, there is abundant evidence that the mechanism involves the dissociation of the halide on the surface followed by surface migration and re-evaporation of the fragments. The simplest case to discuss is that in which all of the steps are in chemical and thermal equilibrium (a thermodynamic treatment of this process has been given elsewhere.[59,71]) In this case the positive ion yield is given by the Saha-Langmuir equation using the ionization potential of the alkali atom and the work function proper for the site of desorption, which may be bare or may be covered with the adsorbed halogen. The ionization efficiencies of the potassium halides (Cl, Br, and I) on pure tungsten at high temperatures ($> 1800°$ K) are essentially identical to that of elemental potassium.[72,73] However, as the temperature is decreased there is an increase in efficiency over the expected value, indicating the formation of a surface of higher work function due to partial coverage with adsorbed halogen. Similar observations on the sodium halides[74] indicate partial surface coverage to even the highest temperatures. Without a knowledge of the heat of adsorption of the alkali at these sites, a precise calculation of the surface coverage is not possible, since the sites with the lowest heat of adsorption will contribute more than their share to the observed ion–atom ratio. However, it is interesting to note that the degree of surface coverage of tungsten by iodide is larger than that by chloride or bromide, which are almost identical, and that fluoride (judged by results on KF)[73] gives an even greater coverage, which, moreover, extends up to 2400° K.

These results may have a bearing on the observations of Trischka, Marple and White,[75] who measured the efficiency of negative ionization of the cesium halides on thoriated tungsten. They found qualitative agreement with the values expected from the electron affinities for chlorine, bromine, and iodine, but found no evidence for fluoride ion emission even though this ion should have shown the highest yield. The formation of a stable, high-work-function fluoride film would have given the observed effect.

Further evidence for dissociation preceding ionization was found by Ionov,[76] who, in measuring the electron affinity of chlorine, found that the ion yield on tungsten of the alkali chlorides was independent of the cation (Na, K, Rb, or Cs). This also indicates no appreciable coverage by the alkali metal after dissociation.

In order to obtain ionization characteristic of the equilibrium state, it is first necessary for the impinging molecule to have a sufficiently strong interaction with the surface. There is now good evidence that this is not true in all systems. Datz and Taylor[73] have observed that the potassium halides are reflected from a platinum surface before dissociation can take place. This reflection amounts to more than 99% for the chloride, bromide, and iodide, and 75% for the fluoride.

In a recent paper, Klemperer and Hershbach[77] have proposed that the rate of dissociation of lithium chloride (and hence its ionization efficiency) at an oxygenated tungsten surface is a function of the vibrational state of the molecule. This argument is based on the experimental observations of Marple and Trischka[78] on the radio frequency spectrum of lithium chloride. In this experiment, separate resonances were observed for four different vibrational states, $\nu = 0$, 1, 2, 3, but the relative populations of these states, as indicated by the ion current, did not correspond to the population distribution calculable from the measured oven temperature. Instead, the ratio of observed to expected relative ion currents increased with increasing vibrational quantum number from a value of 1 (normalized) for $\nu = 0$ to 1.4, 2.0 and 2.9 for $\nu = 1$, 2, and 3, respectively. To explain this, Klemperer and Hershbach considered the dissociation in terms of a stepwise excitation of vibrational levels of the molecule at the surface and showed that the probability of dissociation before desorption should

M

be higher for vibrationally excited molecules. The values of the ratios calculated from this model gave good agreement with the experimental results. This approach may, in the future, yield much information on the role of vibrational states in reaction kinetics.

Gas–Gas Interactions

A complete understanding of the mechanics of chemical reactions depends ultimately on our knowledge of the forces experienced by potentially reactive molecules. Although in principle all of these interactions are exactly calculable from the quantum mechanics, the mathematical difficulties of this approach cause us to rely on empirical evidence. The bulk of our knowledge of intermolecular potentials has come from statistical interpretations of macroscopic equilibrium and transport properties, and in the case of reactive collisions from measurements of reaction rates as a function of temperature. The possibility of gaining additional information from studies of the effects of single collisions on molecules contained in unidirectional beams of controlled energy has been the motivation for the investigations that will be discussed.

The forces involved may be divided into three groups: first, the relatively long-range attractive forces which arise from the interactions of permanent or induced electric dipoles; second, the short-range Pauli repulsive forces caused by electron overlap; third, the complex interactions involved in chemically reactive collisions.

Since the molecular beam method allows measurement of very small deflections, the collision cross section defined by a measurement of the attenuation of a well-defined beam passing through a gas-filled scattering chamber is a measure of the maximum interaction sphere between two molecules. This maximum interaction sphere is determined by the van der Waals attractive potential of the form $V(r) \sim -C/r^6$. Massey and Mohr[79] have shown that the constant, C, is derivable from a measurement of the total cross section. The numbers obtained from measured collision radii of alkali atoms in rare gases have been found to be in good agreement with the values calculated from the polarizabilities of the atoms. These results are well covered in other works[2,4,23] and will not be repeated here. However, it may be noted that all the collisions studied thus far have been between atoms or non-polar molecules, in which C is determined exclusively by dispersion forces. It is therefore suggested that valuable information on the coupling of dipole-dipole, dipole-induced dipole, and induced dipole-induced dipole forces could be gained from measurements of beam collision cross sections in which either one or both of the colliding species has a sufficiently large permanent dipole moment to contribute appreciably to the total potential.

If the velocity of the beam is increased above the thermal range, the total cross section becomes less affected by the weak van der Waals attraction and is defined more by the repulsive overlap forces. Amdur and his co-workers have developed techniques for measurement of total scattering cross sections for such high-velocity (200 to 2000 ev) atomic beams. The beam is obtained by the electron attachment neutralization of an ion beam extracted from an arc source. The resultant atom beam is then passed through a scattering chamber and is detected by a thermoelement consisting of either a vacuum thermopile or a bolometer.

The first work of this type was done in an apparatus designed by Amdur and Pearlman[80] on the systems He–He,[81] A–A,[82] H–H₂,[83,84] and D–D₂.[84] A much improved apparatus[85] was constructed in which beam profiles could be measured, and the results reported from this machine are summarized in Table 2, where the parameters K and S are related to the potential by $V(r) = K/r^S(\text{erg})$ and r (in Å) refers to the range of internuclear distances over which the measurements were made.

TABLE 2
PARAMETERS DEFINING REPULSIVE POTENTIALS
(Amdur and co-workers)

	System	K	S	$r(\text{Å})$	Reference
1	He–He	7.55×10^{-12}	5.94	1.27–1.59	86
2	Ne–Ne	5.00×10^{-10}	9.99	1.76–2.13	87
3	A–A	1.36×10^{-9}	8.33	2.18–2.69	88
4	Kr–Kr	2.55×10^{-10}	5.42	2.42–3.14	89
5	Xe–Xe	1.33×10^{-8}	7.97	3.01–3.60	90
6	He–H	3.75×10^{-12}	3.29	1.16–1.17	91
7	He–A	9.95×10^{-11}	7.25	1.64–2.27	92
8	Ne–A	1.01×10^{-9}	9.18	1.91–2.44	93
9	He–N₂	1.19×10^{-10}	7.06	1.79–2.29	94
10	A–N₂	1.21×10^{-9}	7.78	2.28–2.83	94
11	N₂–N₂	9.54×10^{-10}	7.27	2.43–3.07	94

These results are entirely consistent with potential functions for the same systems at larger distances, derived from gas compressibility and viscosity and from crystal properties, and are in reasonable agreement with theory in those cases for which calculations are possible.[86,92] It is noteworthy that the potential functions of mixed systems can apparently be defined by the geometric mean of the potentials for the homogeneous systems. This postulate, together with a theoretical model for the center of force in the N_2 molecule, was used in calculating the N_2–N_2 potential from He–N_2 and A–N_2.[94]

The use of molecular beam techniques for studies of homogeneous chemical reactions has long been proposed as a means for separating the individual steps involved in observable chemical reactions. However, since most reactions have an activation energy which is high compared to the average collision energy in thermal systems, and since a large number of reactions have appreciable entropies of activation, the probability of reaction on single collision is bound to be small. Therefore, if one hopes to observe the effect of single collisions, one must either choose systems of low activation energy or supply additional energy to one of the reactants.

The initial impetus for studying reactions with beams came from attempts to test the now defunct "Radiation Hypothesis" for unimolecular chemical reactions.[95] This theory postulated that the activation energy was not supplied by collisions but instead by absorption of infrared radiation from the walls of the reaction vessel.

The experiments consisted of measuring the degree of chemical change occurring in a beam of reactant that had been exposed to thermal radiation upon passing through a heated tube. Thus, Kröger[96] looked for an attenuation of an iodine beam due to dissociation in flight, Mayer[97,98] attempted to determine the degree of internal racemization of pinene by polarimetric analysis of the beam deposit, and Rice, Urey, and Washburne[99] tried to measure the dissociation of nitrogen pentoxide by determining the amount of nitrite formed from a beam deposit. In all these cases negative results were recorded, and although some objections have been raised to their validity,[1] they helped to contribute to the demise of the "Radiation Hypothesis".

In the field of bimolecular chemical reactions, most of the beam work thus far has given very poor results, due either to poor choice of systems or to incorrect interpretation of the results. The first work of this type was done by Kröger,[96] who attempted to measure reactions occurring at the intersection of a beam of cadmium with a beam of iodine or sulfur. The degree of reaction was estimated by two different techniques: first, by measuring the amount of product deposited in an angle between the two beams, and second, by using the rate of evaporation of liquid oxygen surrounding the reaction vessel to measure the heat liberated in the reaction. Unfortunately, the limitations of chemical analysis led him to raise the intensity too far for good definition, and the excessive elastic scattering probably masked any reaction products. This type of reaction seems also a poor choice for study. The activation energy should be appreciable since both of the reaction partners are electronically non-degenerate and the attainment of the intermediate state should at the least require electronic excitation of one of the valence electrons of the cadmium. In addition, the formation of CdI_2 on collision would not occur without a three-body collision to remove the energy of reaction, and only the formation of the sub-halide (CdI), by exchange, would be possible.

TABLE 3

COMPARISON OF CROSS SECTIONS BY SASAKI (S) WITH THOSE OF ROSIN AND RABI AND ROSENBERG (R)

Atom Beam	Scattering gas	Cross section (Å)² (S)	(R)	Reference (S)	(R)
	Ne		213		103
	A		401		103
Na	N_2	132		105	
	O_2	118		105	
	Cl_2	78.8		106	
	H_2	191	198	107, 108, 109	104
	A	452	587	107, 108, 109	104
K	N_2	467	613	107, 108, 109	104
	O_2	460		107, 108, 109	
	Cl_2	571		109	

Sasaki and his co-workers have reported observations on a large number of potentially reactive systems. The motivation for this work was the extremely high collision yield obtained for alkali metal-halogen reactions by dilute flame and diffusion flame techniques,[100] which indicated that the reaction cross section was somewhat higher than the kinetic theory cross section.[101] Sasaki, therefore, set out to measure the absolute beam collision cross sections of these components with the hope of observing larger cross sections than the predicted values. However, even if these large reaction cross sections exist, they still are smaller than the elastic scattering cross sections defined by a beam experiment. Hence, these measurements do not indicate any features of the reactive collision except that the molecules do not react outside the sphere of influence of van der Waals forces. A further demonstration of this was an experiment in which the relative cross section of sodium with naphthalene and with iodine was found to be in agreement with the gas kinetic ratio.[102] The cross sections observed by Sasaki are shown in Table 3 together with some values on comparable systems by Rosin and Rabi,[103] and by Rosenberg.[104]

Where the same pairs of molecules were measured by both sets of investigators, the cross sections by Sasaki, *et al.*, are lower, perhaps because of poorer angular resolution. A much greater disparity can be seen by extrapolation to exist between the sodium cross sections of the two groups. Since the values of Rosin snd Rabi are consistent with calculations from polarizability [4,23] as well as being internally consistent, one can only suppose some systematic error to exist in Sasaki's measurements. The lack of detail in his publications make it fruitless to speculate on the cause.

In a conceptually interesting experiment, Nishibori and Sasaki[110,111] claim to have observed evidence for an extraordinarily large cross section for reaction of beams of vibrationally excited iodine molecules with mercury. In this work, a molecular beam of iodine was crossed at right angles with a beam of light, or with an atomic beam of mercury, or with both simultaneously. The vibrational excitation of the symmetric iodine molecule was induced by electronic excitation with light, followed by fluorescence to excited vibrational levels in the electronic ground state. When the iodine molecular beam was crossed with a light beam, there was an observable attenuation (0.4%) which was attributed to dissociation. The relative cross sections of the vibrationally excited and of the normal molecules were determined by measuring the attenuation obtained from a cross beam of mercury with the light beam on and off. The total attenuation was found to be greater than the sum of the individual attenuations due either to mercury or to light alone. From this, the ratio of collision diameters for excited to ground state iodine molecules in mercury was found to be: $\sigma_{I_2}*/\sigma_{I_2} = 2.56$. The authors postulated that this enormous increase might be attributed to a large cross section for chemical reaction in the excited state. However, the precision claimed (1 part in 10^5) is completely unwarranted by the experimental arrangement, involving a quartz torsion balance detector, and a reasonable estimate of the experimental error would barely allow observation of the attenuation by light and would completely mask any determination of relative cross sections.

Recently some studies have been made on the initiation of elementary chemical processes by passing a high-temperature molecular beam into a low-temperature reaction gas, thereby supplying extra collision energy to an otherwise metastable system. In the experimental arrangement used by Martin and co-workers, the beam is formed in a high-temperature oven and enters a glass reaction vessel, the walls of which are held at room temperature. The gas with which the beam is to collide flows through the reaction vessel at a pressure such that a beam molecule makes only one collision on the average before hitting the wall, where it is presumably deactivated. The gas is frozen out in a trap after flowing through the reaction vessel, and the amount of reaction determined by chemical analysis. Using this system, Martin and Meyer[112] have studied the unimolecular decomposition of ClO_2 induced by collision with molecular beams of I_2 and of $C_2F_3Cl_3$. The postulated mechanism for the homogeneous decomposition is the initial activation of ClO_2 by collision with the high-temperature beam molecule

$$ClO_2 + M \rightarrow ClO_2{}^* + M \tag{1}$$

followed by unimolecular decomposition

$$ClO_2{}^* \rightarrow Cl + O_2. \tag{2}$$

The chlorine atom is then adsorbed at the wall where it combines with another chlorine atom and leaves the reaction vessel as Cl_2. The observed collision yield at first increased with increasing beam temperature, but began to fall off near 700° K. This surprising decline is totally inexplicable by a simple mechanism, and is attributed by the authors to the possible formation of a metastable excited state of the molecule. Since the walls are undoubtedly covered with adsorbed ClO_2, it is unfortunate that this method does not eliminate the possibility of wall reactions. Thus the reactions

$$M + ClO_2(\text{adsorbed}) \rightarrow M + Cl + O_2 \tag{3}$$

and

$$Cl + ClO_2(\text{adsorbed}) \rightarrow Cl_2 + O_2 \tag{4}$$

may occur, and the anomalous behavior of the collision yield may be the result of a complex chain reaction involving steps at the wall.

Similar objections can be raised to results of the work by Martin and Diskowski,[113] who reacted a high-temperature beam of hydrogen atoms (from thermal dissociation of H_2) with chlorine gas to study the reaction

$$H + Cl_2 \rightarrow HCl + Cl. \tag{5}$$

They calculated an activation energy of 9.4 kcal/mol from measurements of the collision yield at two beam temperatures. The possible competing and complicating wall reactions occurring here are those of the hydrogen beam atom with an adsorbed chlorine molecule

$$H + Cl_2(\text{adsorbed}) \rightarrow HCl + Cl \tag{6}$$

and of the chlorine atom formed by either reaction (5) or (6) with an adsorbed hydrogen atom.

A mechanical method for activation of fast reactions has been developed by Bull and Moon.[114] Gas molecules are accelerated by momentary contact with the tip of a rotating blade and are then collimated into a high-velocity pulsed beam. Peripheral velocities of up to 10^5 cm sec^{-1} are attainable in such a device, and heavy molecules such as carbon tetrachloride traveling at this velocity carry energies of the order of 10 kcal/mol. The experiment reported employed a pulsed, accelerated beam of CCl_4 and an ionization gage as detector. The latter was biased to measure electrons and negative ions, and the pulse shape and transit time of the excess current due to negative ions were observed on an oscilloscope triggered by the source rotor. A scattering region, previously evacuated, was then filled with Cs vapor, the detector polarity was reversed to measure positive-ion current from surface ionization, and the pulses arising from Cs or CsCl scattered forward into the detector were examined. The relative pulse transit times were interpreted as indicating considerable reaction, but the absence of direct differentiation between Cs and CsCl was recognized as an obfuscating factor. The use of a differential surface ionization detector[115] might help to bring to realization the potentialities of this method of activation.

A crossed-beam method was employed by Taylor and Datz[115] in studying the reaction of potassium and hydrogen bromide, which had been thought to proceed on every collision.[100] In this work, in-flight detection of the collision product was made possible by the use of a surface ionization gage containing a platinum and a tungsten filament. The tungsten surface ionized the reaction product (KBr) and the elastically scattered potassium with nearly equal efficiency, while the platinum surface ionized essentially only the unreacted potassium. The flux of KBr at any angle could therefore be obtained from measurements with each of the filaments and a knowledge of the relative efficiencies for ionization. The total yield of KBr could be obtained by integration of these measurements over the proper angular region. Measurement of this yield as a function of beam temperatures and use of the proper distribution function for energies of collision yielded the activation energy (3.4 kcal/mol). Measurement of the total collision cross section and the reaction yield, combined with an estimate of the kinetic theory cross section, yielded the conventional steric factor (~ 0.1). Measurement of the angular distribution of the product permitted a qualitative interpretation of the configuration of the reaction intermediate. A detailed comparison of the angular distribution of reaction product with that predicted by models for the activated complex appears to be impossible without more nearly mono-energetic collisions. Some improvement can be made fairly easily by monochromatization of one component at high energy and reduction of the energy spread of the other by holding its source at low temperature.

Use of the crossed-beam technique to study the details of combustion reactions of interest in rocket propulsion was proposed recently by Sänger-Bredt[116] in a review of experimental methods in high-temperature reaction kinetics.

Now that several experiments attest the feasibility of using molecular beams in chemical kinetics, it may be worth while to suggest directions for future research. Two general lines of development seem to be indicated. First is the use of as much of the beam technique as possible on a variety of reactions, in order to give, if only qualitatively, a comparison, over a range of reactions, of activation energies and steric factors measured under these unambiguous conditions, and of angular distributions, which can be measured only by the crossed-beam technique. The chief problem here is detection, but there is a whole host of reactions[117] for which the differential surface ionization gage[115] may suffice, and there is hope of extending this method and the "universal" (mass-spectrometric) detector[4] to other systems. Some of these reactions may be suitable for partial energy selection, and some perhaps for photo-excitation of particular energy states, while in others some energy analysis of a product species may be possible.

The second line is to apply the complete molecular beam technique to a single reaction simple enough that complete calculations from first principles are available for comparison with experiment. This effectively limits the possible reactants to hydrogen atoms, ions and molecules and suggests two possible reactions

$$H + D_2 = HD + D$$

and

$$H^+ + D_2 = HD + D^+.$$

These appear feasible, and are presently under study.[118]

REFERENCES

[1] R. G. J. Fraser, "Molecular Rays," Cambridge University Press, Cambridge, 1931.

[2] R. G. J. Fraser, "Molecular Beams," Methuen and Co., Ltd., London, 1937.

[3] W. H. Bessey and O. C. Simpson, *Chem. Rev.* **30**, 239 (1942).

[4] N. F. Ramsey, "Molecular Beams," Oxford University Press, Oxford, 1956.

[5] O. Stern, *Z. Physik* **2**, 49 (1920); **3**, 417 (1920).

[6] I. F. Zartman, *Phys. Rev.* **37**, 383 (1931).

178   SHELDON DATZ AND ELLISON H. TAYLOR

[7] C. C. Ko, *Phys. Rev.* **44**, 129 (1933), and *J. Franklin nst.* **217**, 173 (1934).
[8] R. C. Miller and P. Kusch, *J. Chem. Phys.* **25**, 860 (1956); **27**, 981 (1957).
[9] A. Leu, *Z. Physik* **49**, 498 (1928).
[10] L. C. Lewis, *Z. Physik* **69**, 786 (1931).
[11] M. Knudsen, *Ann. Physik* **29**, 179 (1909).
[12] I. Langmuir, *Phys. Rev.* **2**, 329 (1913).
[13] W. A. Chupka and M. G. Inghram, *J. Phys. Chem.* **59**, 100 (1955).
[14] C. L. McCabe, H. M. Schadel, Jr., and C. E. Birchenall, *J. Metals* **5**, 709 (1953).
[15] S. Datz and R. E. Minturn, USAEC Report ORNL-2046 (1955).
[16] G. C. Eltenton, *J. Chem. Phys.* **10**, 403 (1942); **15**, 455 (1947).
[17] P. D. Zemany and M. Burton, *J. Phys. & Colloid Chem.* **55**, 949 (1951).
[18] G. B. Kistiakowsky and P. H. Kydd, *J. Am. Chem. Soc.* **79**, 4825 (1957).
[19] A. J. B. Robertson, *Proc. Roy. Soc. (London)* A **199**, 394 (1949).
[20] S. N. Foner and R. L. Hudson, *J. Chem. Phys.* **23**, 1364 (1955).
[21] J. L. Costa, H. D. Smyth, and K. T. Compton, *Phys. Rev.* **30**, 349 (1927).
[22] J. E. Lennard-Jones and A. F. Devonshire, *Proc. Roy. Soc. (London)* A **156**, 37 (1936).
[23] H. S. W. Massey and E. H. S. Burhop, "Electronic and Ionic Impact Phenomena," Oxford University Press, New York, 1952.
[24] J. E. Lennard-Jones and A. F. Devonshire, *Proc. Roy. Soc. (London)* A **156**, 6 (1936).
[25] L. Yang, M. T. Simnad, and G. M. Pound, *Acta Met.* **2**, 470 (1954).
[26] L. Yang, C. E. Birchenall, G. M. Pound, and M. T. Simnad, *Acta Met.* **2**, 462 (1954).
[27] H. Frauenfelder, *Helv. Phys. Acta* **23**, 347 (1950).
[28] J. D. Cockroft, *Proc. Roy. Soc. (London)* A **119**, 306 (1928).
[29] I. Estermann, *Z. Elektrochem.* **31**, 441 (1925).
[30] J. D. Cockroft, *Proc. Roy. Soc. (London)* A **119**, 295 (1928).
[31] G. Ribaud and F. M. Devienne, *Compt. rend.* **230**, 1811 (1950); **231**, 740 (1950).
[32] F. M. Devienne, *Compt. rend.* **232**, 1088 (1952); **234**, 80 (1952); **238**, 2397 (1954), and *J. Phys. Radium* **13**, 53 (1952); **14**, 257 (1953).
[33] F. M. Devienne, *Compt. rend.* **239**, 1202 (1954).
[34] P. Garin and P. Prugne, *J. Phys. Radium* **15**, 829 (1954).
[35] N. D. Morgulis, V. M. Gavrilyuk, and A. E. Kulik, *Doklady Akad. Nauk S.S.S.R* **101**, 479 (1955).
[36] L. Brewer and D. F. Mastick, USAEC Report UCRL-572 (1949).
[37] O. C. Simpson, R. J. Thorn, and G. H. Winslow, USAEC Report ANL-4264 (1949).
[38] S. Wexler, Brookhaven National Laboratory Molecular Beam Conference, August, 1954.
[39] R. S. Bradley and P. Volans, *Proc. Roy. Soc. (London)* A **217**, 508 (1953).
[40] R. S. Bradley, *Proc. Roy. Soc. (London)* A **217**, 524 (1953).
[41] L. Frank, *Trans. Faraday Soc.* **32**, 1403 (1936).
[42] I. Estermann, *Z. Physik Chem.* **106**, 403 (1923).
[43] J. D. Cockroft, *Proc. Roy. Soc. (London)* A **119**, 293 (1928).
[44] M. C. Johnson and T. V. Starkey, *Proc. Roy. Soc. (London)* A **140**, 126 (1933).
[45] T. V. Starkey, *Phil. Mag.* **18**, 241 (1934).
[46] N. T. Melnikova, E. D. Shchukin, and M. M. Umonskii, *Zhur. Eksptl. i Teoret. Fiz.* **22**, 775 (1952).
[47] H. N. Alyea and F. Haber, *Naturwiss.* **18**, 441 (1930).

[48] M. Bodenstein, *Trans. Electrochem. Soc.* **71**, 353 (1937).

[49] F. O. Rice and H. T. Byck, *Proc. Roy. Soc. (London)* A **132**, 50 (1931).

[50] O. Beeck, *Nature* **136**, 1028 (1935).

[51] O. Beeck, *Revs. Mod. Phys.* **20**, 127 (1948).

[52] J. Dewing and A. J. B. Robertson, *Discuss. Faraday Soc.* **17**, 102 (1954).

[53] P. Clausing, *Physica* **8**, 289 (1928).

[54] O. Beeck, *J. Chem. Phys.* **4**, 680 (1936).

[55] N. Sasaki, K. Taku and K. Mitani, *Mem. Coll. Sci. Univ. Kyoto*, Ser. A **25**, No. 2, 75 (1949).

[56] I. Langmuir and K. H. Kingdon, *Proc. Roy. Soc. (London)* A **107**, 61 (1925).

[57] J. A. Becker, *Trans. Am. Electrochem. Soc.* **55**, 153 (1929), and *Ann. N.Y. Acad. Sci.* **58**, 723 (1954).

[58] L. N. Dobretsov, "Elektronen- und Ionenemission," VEB Verlag Technik, Berlin, 1954 (translated from Russian edition dated 1952).

[59] B. H. Zimm and J. E. Mayer, *J. Chem. Phys.* **12**, 362 (1944).

[60] S. Datz and E. H. Taylor, *J. Chem. Phys.* **25**, 389 (1956).

[61] J. B. Taylor, *Z. Physik* **57**, 242 (1929).

[62] M. Inghram, "Modern Mass Spectroscopy," *in* "Advances in Electronics," Vol. I (L. Marton, ed.), Academic Press, Inc., New York, 1948.

[63] J. B. Taylor and I. Langmuir, *Phys. Rev.* **44**, 423 (1933).

[64] J. H. de Boer, "The Dynamical Character of Adsorption," Oxford University Press, New York, 1953.

[65] R. C. Evans, *Proc. Roy. Soc. (London)* A **139**, 604 (1933).

[66] S. V. Starodubtsev, *Zhur. Eksptl. i Teoret. Fiz.* **19**, 215 (1949).

[67] F. Knauer, *Z. Physik* **125**, 278 (1948).

[68] L. Pauling, "The Nature of the Chemical Bond," Cornell University Press, Ithaca, N.Y., 1944.

[69] F. Hughes and H. Levinstein, Syracuse University Research Inst., Technical Report, Sept., 1956.

[70] L. N. Dobretsov, S. V. Starodubtsev and J. I. Timokhina, *Compt. rend. acad. sci. U.R.S.S.* **55**, 303 (1947).

[71] G. E. Cogin and G. E. Kimball, *J. Chem. Phys.* **16**, 1035 (1948).

[72] J. O. Hendricks, T. E. Phipps and M. J. Copley, *J. Chem. Phys.* **5**, 868 (1937).

[73] S. Datz and E. H. Taylor, *J. Chem. Phys.* **25**, 395 (1956).

[74] A. A. Johnson and T. E. Phipps, *J. Chem. Phys.* **7**, 1039 (1939).

[75] J. W. Trischka, D. T. F. Marple, and A. White, *Phys. Rev.* **85**, 136 (1952).

[76] N. I. Ionov, *Zhur. Eksptl. i Teoret. Fiz.* **18**, 174 (1948).

[77] W. Klemperer and D. Herschbach, *Proc. Natl. Acad. Sci.* **43**, 429 (1957).

[78] D. T. F. Marple and J. W. Trischka, *Phys. Rev.* **103**, 597 (1956).

[79] H. S. W. Massey and C. B. O. Mohr, *Proc. Roy. Soc. (London)* A **141**, 434 (1933); A **144**, 188 (1934).

[80] I. Amdur and H. Pearlman, *J. Chem. Phys.* **8**, 7 (1940).

[81] I. Amdur and H. Pearlman, *J. Chem. Phys.* **9**, 503 (1941).

[82] I. Amdur, D. E. Davenport, and M. C. Kells, *J. Chem. Phys.* **18**, 525 (1950).

[83] I. Amdur, *J. Chem. Phys.* **11**, 157 (1943).

[84] I. Amdur, M. C. Kells, and D. E. Davenport, *J. Chem. Phys.* **18**, 1676 (1950).

[85] I. Amdur, C. F. Glick, and H. Pearlman, *Proc. Am. Acad. Arts Sci.* **76**, 101 (1948).

[86] I. Amdur and A. L. Harkness, *J. Chem. Phys.* **22**, 664 (1954).

[87] I. Amdur and E. A. Mason, *J. Chem. Phys.* **23**, 415 (1955).

[88] I. Amdur and E. A. Mason, *J. Chem. Phys.* **22**, 670 (1954).

[89] I. Amdur and E. A. Mason, *J. Chem. Phys.* **23**, 2268 (1955).
[90] I. Amdur and E. A. Mason, *J. Chem. Phys.* **25**, 624 (1956).
[91] I. Amdur and E. A. Mason, *J. Chem. Phys.* **25**, 630 (1956).
[92] I. Amdur, E. A. Mason and A. L. Harkness, *J. Chem. Phys.* **22**, 1071 (1954).
[93] I. Amdur and E. A. Mason, *J. Chem. Phys.* **25**, 632 (1956).
[94] I. Amdur, E. A. Mason, and J. E. Jordan, *J. Chem. Phys.* **27**, 527 (1957).
[95] L. S. Kassel, "Kinetics of Homogeneous Gas Reactions," Reinhold Publishing Corp., New York, 1932.
[96] M. Kröger, *Z. Physik. Chem.* **117**, 387 (1925).
[97] J. E. Mayer, *J. Am. Chem. Soc.* **49**, 3033 (1927).
[98] G. N. Lewis and J. E. Mayer, *Proc. Natl. Acad. Sci.* **13**, 623 (1927).
[99] F. O. Rice, H. C. Urey, and R. N. Washburne, *J. Am. Chem. Soc.* **50**, 2402 (1928).
[100] M. Polanyi, "Atomic Reactions," Williams and Norgate, London, 1932.
[101] J. L. Magee, *J. Chem. Phys.* **8**, 687 (1940).
[102] E. Nishibori, *J. Chem. Soc. Japan* **57**, 1291 (1936).
[103] S. Rosin and I. I. Rabi, *Phys. Rev.* **48**, 373 (1935).
[104] P. Rosenberg, *Phys. Rev.* **55**, 1267 (1939).
[105] N. Sasaki, E. Nishibori, G. Kondo, and K. Kodera, *J. Chem. Soc. Japan* **57**, 1284 (1936).
[106] N. Sasaki, E. Nishibori, and H. Uchida, *J. Chem. Soc. Japan* **57**, 1277 (1936).
[107] K. Kodera, *J. Chem. Soc. Japan* **65**, 645 (1944); **66**, 52 (1945); **67**, 80 (1946).
[108] N. Sasaki and K. Kodera, *Proc. Imp. Acad.* (*Tokio*) **17**, 70 (1941).
[109] N. Sasaki and K. Kodera, *Mem. Coll. Sci. Univ. Kyoto*, Ser. A **25**, No. 2, 83 (1949).
[110] E. Nishibori, *J. Chem. Soc. Japan* **58**, 4 (1937); **58**, 14 (1937).
[111] N. Sasaki and E. Nishibori, *Proc. Imp. Acad.* (*Tokio*) **12**, 10 (1936).
[112] H. Martin and H.-J. Meyer, *Z. Elektrochem.* **56**, 740 (1952), and *Naturwiss.* **39**, 85 (1952).
[113] H. Martin and H. Diskowski, *Z. Elektrochem.* **60**, 964 (1956).
[114] T. H. Bull and P. B. Moon, *Discuss. Faraday Soc.* **17**, 54 (1954).
[115] E. H. Taylor and S. Datz, *J. Chem. Phys.* **23**, 1711 (1955).
[116] I. Sänger-Bredt, *Astronaut. Acta* **1**, 1 (1955).
[117] C. E. H. Bawn, *Chem. Soc. Ann. Repts.* **39**, 36 (1942).
[118] S. Datz and E. H. Taylor, USAEC Report ORNL-2386 (1957).

10

A Stern-Gerlach Experiment on Polarized Neutrons*

J. E. SHERWOOD, T. E. STEPHENSON, and SEYMOUR BERNSTEIN

Oak Ridge National Laboratory, Oak Ridge, Tennessee

Introduction

When a beam of neutrons passes through a material body the process may be considered analogous to the passage of light through a refractive medium. Thus we may define an index of refraction $n = \sqrt{(E-V/E)}$, where E is the energy of a neutron, and V is the average potential energy of the neutron while in the body. If θ is the glancing angle of incidence, it follows that total reflection will occur for $\theta = \sqrt{(V/E)}$. In other words, all wavelengths greater than the critical wave length

$$\lambda_c = \theta\sqrt{\frac{h^2}{2mV}}$$

will be totally reflected.

In the case of a magnetized iron mirror, the potential energy is $V = V_n + V_m$, where V_n is that due to the nuclei and $V_m = -\bar{\mu}\cdot\bar{B}$ is the potential energy of the neutron's magnetic moment $\bar{\mu}$ in the average net field $\bar{B}$. Thus, if λ^+_c and λ^-_c are the critical wavelengths for $\bar{\mu}$ parallel to $\bar{B}$ and $\bar{\mu}$ antiparallel to $\bar{B}$ respectively, we have that

$$\lambda^+_c > \lambda^-_c \quad (B\neq 0)$$

The spectrum of reflected neutrons will therefore have the general appearance shown in Fig. 1 (assuming the spectrum of the incident beam to be Maxwellian). Thus the spin state with $\bar{\mu}$ antiparallel to $\bar{B}$ is more abundant. Since the gyromagnetic ratio of the neutron is negative,[1] the resultant spin of the neutrons in the totally reflected beam is parallel to the applied magnetic field. It may be noted that the direction of the dominant neutron spin in a beam of

*Reprinted from *Physical Review*.

polarized neutrons is significant in the interpretation of experiments on the interaction of polarized neutron beams with polarized target nuclei.[2,3] However, in no other experiments with polarized neutrons has the direction of the neutron spin been of consequence. Only neutron intensities were involved.

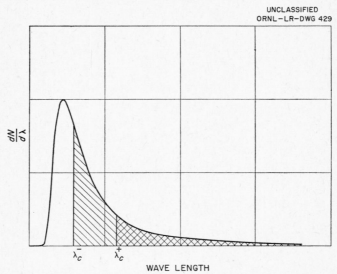

UNCLASSIFIED
ORNL−LR−DWG 429

Fig. 1. Intensity distribution of neutrons reflected from magnetized iron mirror. For μ parallel to $\overline{B}$, $\lambda > \lambda^+{}_c$. For μ anti-parallel to $\overline{B}$, $\lambda > \lambda^-{}_c$.

In order to check the results of the above argument in a very direct manner, we have done a Stern-Gerlach type of experiment in which a beam of polarized neutrons is deflected magnetically. This experiment is described below.

Description of the Apparatus

The mirror was of soft iron, about $1\frac{3}{4}$ in. × 6 in. long and was magnetized parallel to the face in a direction perpendicular to the length and to the neutron beam. The exit edge of the mirror was rounded off so that the magnetic field in this region would change less abruptly. It was felt that this procedure would partially alleviate the depolarization effects found by early experimenters. The glancing angle of the neutron beam upon the mirror was approximately 3.10^{-3} radians.

The slot-wedge type of deflecting field was felt to give the highest gradient consistent with reasonable cost. Since this arrangement had been thoroughly investigated by the early molecular beam experimenters,[4] the cross section of their magnet gap was copied. Fig. 2[5] describes the cross section and magnetic characteristics of the gap; the length chosen was 1 meter. The average field in our magnet gap was found to be about 20,000 Oersteds by means of a bismuth wire measurement. Energy for the gap was provided by four large solenoids of about 13,000 ampere turns each.

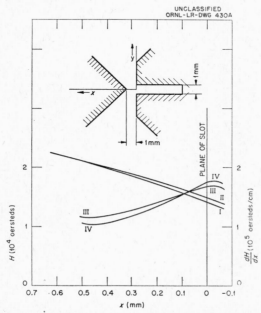

Fig. 2. Field strength and inhomogeneity of magnetic field in gap (ref. 5): Curve I: Field strength in the plane of symmetry. Curve II: Field strength of 0.2 mm outside plane of symmetry. Curve III: Inhomogeneity in the plane of symmetry. Curve IV: Inhomogeneity 0.2 mm outside plane of symmetry.

The detector was a conventional arrangement consisting of a well-shielded BF_3 counter of about 1 in. diameter and 8 in. long. Its efficiency was about 90% for the reflected neutrons. Standard amplifiers and a scale-of-64 registers were used. Background was 1.6 counts/min.

Even with a gradient of the order of 10^5 Oersted/cm extended over a length of a meter, the deflections produced are inconveniently small. This, together with the difficulty of producing such a gradient over a large space, requires a very high degree of collimation, in order to ensure that only those neutrons which spend an appreciable length of time in the region of high gradient will be counted. This was achieved, as shown in Fig. 3, by a combination of cadmium slits and holes. The main collimation was provided by the 0.010 in. vertical slit at the exit end of the deflecting magnet. It is easily seen that this location of the slit does not complicate the interpretation of the results and leads to much better collimation than is obtained with the slit preceding the deflecting magnet.

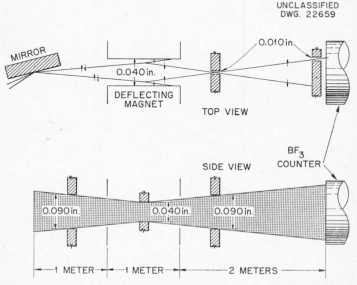

UNCLASSIFIED
DWG. 22659

Fig. 3. Schematic diagram of beam collimation system showing typical trajectories and vertical slits (top view) and horizontal slits (side view).

Procedure

The two spin-states will suffer opposite forces in the deflecting magnet so that, with perfect collimation and infinitely good resolution, one should obtain an intensity distribution in the beam as shown in Fig. 4. (Displacement is proportional to λ^2.)

In practice, however, a 0.010 in. slit is translated across the face of the detector and yields the result shown in Fig. 5. For comparative purposes, undeflected and deflected-depolarized beams are shown there also. The depolarization was accomplished by interposing a soft iron shim in the beam between the mirror and the deflecting magnet, at a place where the magnetic field was small.

The experiment was repeated under conditions in which the neutron spins were "flipped" relative to the magnetic field, during their passage

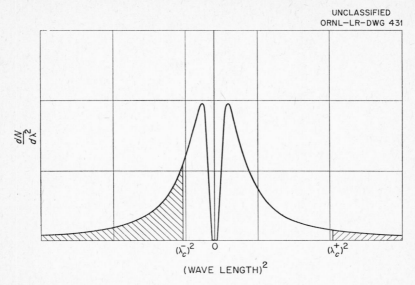

Fig. 4. Expected deflection pattern for infinite resolving power and perfect collimation. Shaded areas are derived from Fig. 1.

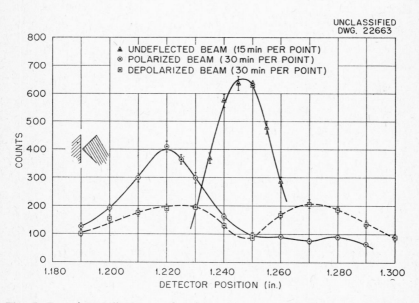

Fig. 5. Experimentally observed deflection patterns. Inset shows orientation of pole-pieces with respect to the intensity pattern.

N

from the mirror to the deflecting magnet. This spin reversal was brought about by means of an arrangement of permanent magnets and pole pieces which caused the field to reverse its direction in a distance short compared with the Larmor precession distance. An intensity-displacement run then yielded the result shown in Fig. 6, in which it is seen that the main portion of the beam is now deflected to the right, instead of to the left.

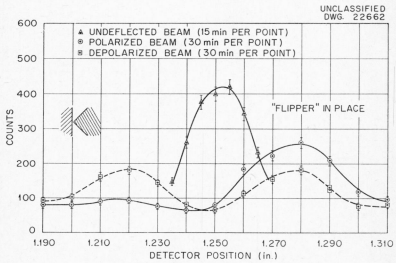

Fig. 6. Deflection pattern for "flipped" beam.

Interpretation of Results

If we consider only the normal pattern, Fig. 5, and agree to take directions to the right as a positive X-axis, the following argument applies: The energy of the dipole is $W = -\bar{\mu} \cdot \bar{H} = -(\bar{\mu} \cdot \hat{H})H$, where $\hat{H}$ is a unit vector in the direction of the magnetic field $\bar{H}$, and H is the magnitude of the field. Then $F_x = -(dW/dx) = (\bar{\mu} \cdot \hat{H})(dH/dx)$. By inspection of Fig. 5, it is seen that $F_x < 0$ and $(dH/dx) > 0$. It follows that $\bar{\mu} \cdot \hat{H} < 0$. Thus the experiment shows directly that the resultant spin in a neutron beam polarized by reflection from magnetized iron is parallel to the magnetic field applied to the mirror.

From this it can be shown that the nuclear and magnetic scattering amplitudes (for iron) are of the same sign when the neutron spin and electronic spin are oppositely directed, and conversely.

By means of double transmission experiments, the resultant spin direction in the totally reflected beam from a magnetized iron mirror was compared with the resultant spin direction produced by transmission through magnetized polycrystalline iron. We find that for a sample magnetized perpendicular to the neutron velocity, the resultant neutron spins are directed opposite to the applied magnetic field. In the case of a single crystal of magnetite, in which the magnetic field was applied perpendicular to the scattering plane, the resultant spin in a beam reflected from the 220 planes was found[6] to be opposite to the applied magnetic field also.

Acknowledgement

We are very grateful to Professor J. M. Jauch for numerous helpful discussions.

REFERENCES

[1] P. N. Powers, *Phys. Rev.* **54**, 827 (1938).
[2] Bernstein, Roberts, Stanford, Dabbs, and Stephenson, *Phys. Rev.* (June 1, 1954).
[3] Roberts, Bernstein, Dabbs, and Stanford, *Phys. Rev.* (July 1, 1954).
[4] I. Estermann and O. Stern, *Z. Physik* **85**, 17 (1933).
[5] *Ibid.*, p. 18.
[6] C. G. Shull, *Phys. Rev.* **81**, 626 (1951).

SUBJECT INDEX

may circulate: